KEEPING A COW

KEEPING A COW

Val Spreckley

DAVID & CHARLES
Newton Abbot   London   North Pomfret (Vt)

British Library Cataloguing in Publication Data

Spreckley, Val
  Keeping a cow.
  1. Cows
  I. Title
  636.2'08'3   SF197

  ISBN 0–7153–7655–1

Library of Congress Catalog Card Number: 78–74083

Set by Northern Phototypesetting Company, Bolton
Printed in Great Britain
by Redwood Burn Limited, Trowbridge and Esher
for David & Charles (Publishers) Limited
Brunel House Newton Abbot Devon

Published in the United States of America
by David & Charles Inc
North Pomfret Vermont 05053 USA

Contents

Foreword and Acknowledgements   7

1 Should You?   9

2 Which Cow?   13

3 Accommodation   22

4 Food   40

5 Milk   50

6 Health   67

7 Calving   80

8 Calf Care   90

9 Produce   99

Appendix   101
Breed Societies, Useful Addresses, Brucellosis Eradication Scheme, Bovine Tuberculosis, Calculation of Rations, Poisonous Plants, Plants which Affect Milk, Breeding

Glossary   115

Book List   117

Index   119

Abbreviations

BF   Butter fat
DM   Dry matter
DVO   District Veterinary Officer
M   Maintenance
MAFF Ministry of Agriculture, Fisheries and Food
ME   Metabolisable energy
MJ   Megajoules
MMB   Milk Marketing Board
PE   Protein equivalent
SE   Starch equivalent
SNF   Solids-not-fat

Foreword and Acknowledgements

This book is for the potential cow owner who has more ingenuity than money. Its intention is to caution as well as to encourage: its role is to temper dreams with realism. Anyone attempting to care for any living thing is dependent as much on luck as on good management, and this book can only influence the latter. Here's luck to you!

My thanks are due to the Milk Marketing Board and to the breed societies, who have provided much useful information as well as photographs of their respective breeds. I am also indebted to Mr David Stadden, MRCVS, for his invaluable advice on chapters 6, 7 and 8, and to Mr Bert Charman and others for many practical tips.

Photographs courtesy of Dexter Cattle Society, Jersey Cattle Society, English Guernsey Cattle Society, Ayrshire Cattle Society, Shorthorn Society, British Friesian Cattle Society and Welsh Black Cattle Society.

1 Should You?

Milk is the most basic of foods, the true *aqua vitae*. It is rich in vitamins A and B and calcium and is a valuable source of protein; its alternative forms, butter and cheese, provide fats for energy and vitamin D. Milk also contains vitamin C, iron, phosphorus and potassium. What more can a body want?

Milk comes ready packaged in bottles and cartons, ready sterilised and homogenised, so clean and dull it is easy to imagine that it was created in a laboratory. It does not have to be like that. If you want to know reality and to gain more than a mere coffee whitener, milk fresh from the udder will satisfy far more than your stomach. Once you have milk on tap, you will also find outlets for creativity, tenderness and bad language: you are back to the roots.

If such an enrichment of your daily life appeals to you, look around for a choice of udders. All mammals produce milk for varying periods after the birth of their young, but for practical purposes man has whittled down his milk suppliers to the ovine and the bovine – sheep, goats and cattle – though for all I know some may prefer mare's milk.

In view of a personal bias against goats and their milk, I have tried to take a firm grip on my prejudice in order to set out clearly the pros and cons of goats versus cows. This book is unashamedly aimed at the cow owner: goat owners already have access to a wealth of information on the care of their animals, and in the fashionable rush into goat-keeping the qualities of the cow have been pushed aside. Goat people have their own societies: house-cow people do not.

A goat is smaller than a cow: it needs less room, it eats less (though it is much fussier) and it produces less milk. It is a browser, preferring leaves to grass, and it can be tethered along the verges (but so can a cow). A goat can be transported by car; billies are reasonably accessible, and kids currently find a very ready market. The milk is easily digested and said to be good for those who suffer from allergies. A bleat is less raucous than a moo, though it tends to be more frequent. Some goats share the fireside with their owners.

Cow's milk tastes as you would expect; goat's milk is an acquired taste. The cream from cow's milk can simply be set and skimmed, but goat's milk must be mechanically separated. A cow can live out all the year round if necessary, but a goat's coat is not waterproof: the animal must not be left out in the rain and should be housed every night whatever the weather. A cow has four teats: if one goes wrong you still have three. A goat has only two teats. A milking cow can, if trained, pull a cart or a load of wood or a plough; a goat cannot. A cow on the whole respects your boundaries; a goat needs tethering (and frequent shifting) or elaborate fencing. A cow is a peaceful animal: her movements tend to be reflective. A goat capers.

Gandhi turned to goat's milk when he became celibate: he said that cow's milk made one feel more sensual.

You would not be reading this book if goats were your preference. But your most basic question must be: 'Do I *like* cows?' You either do or you do not. If you think you might, make a point of seeing cows at their worst: they can be perverse, panicky and mulish, and the odd individual can be far from placid. Remember that cows *are* individuals.

If you do favour a cow, check your assets. There are obvious basic requirements: summer grazing, some form of shelter somewhere, winter fodder – all these require land, whether owned or rented, and you will need at the very least an acre per cow, depending on soil, site and elevation. (I rent a field in exchange for milk: barter whenever you can.) You need access to the means to cultivate your land – a tractor or horse and attachments for sowing your grass, fertilising or muck-spreading, cutting and baling hay. I have tried working my two acres literally by hand, which is fine if you have a lot of time and stamina and no wise-cracking neighbours. Contractors charge disproportionately for small areas of land and tend to be unavailable when you need them most. Nothing is as simple as most books tell you it will be.

Most important of all, you must live near an experienced hand-milker willing to take over if you are badly hungover, genuinely ill, or in need every other year of a short holiday. Your cow normally needs milking twice a day *every day of the year* except for the six or eight weeks before calving when she is dry; and the milk needs consuming.

You should, from the start, encourage your neighbours to take an active, friendly interest in your livestock: they will then be more tolerant towards the bawling of a cow ready for the bull ('bulling') or of a separated mother and calf. And you must have a use for the milk: you will be swimming in anything up to four or five gallons a day at peak times after calving. There will also be several tons of rich and valuable manure which you will be labouring to clear during the winter months. You need somewhere under cover for milking in bad weather, and you need a large kitchen or dairy to cope with the produce. Do not underestimate the milk flow. Other useful assets are a reliable vet and a friendly countryman who handled cows before machines took over.

Time is another factor. On average you will probably spend an hour or more a day, part morning and part evening, on milking, feeding and cleaning up. To process the produce in your 'dairy' might use up four hours a week if you are enthusiastic. Haymaking is full-time work for a week or so each year.

If you are still enthusiastic, read on. My intention is to warn you of the problems and the pitfalls, but if your enthusiasm is genuine these will not deter you. It might help to do a spell as a Milk Marketing Board recorder, in order to gain indirect experience of cows at their worst at 5am on a cold winter morning. The job is tedious and not well paid, the hours are anti-social, but you will get a chance to learn quite a lot about cows without making a full-time job of it. Or get on good terms with the local vet and offer to assist on his rounds: that way you really will learn a lot.

Remember that a cow is a herd animal: it is not fair to keep her on her own. Give her your own company as much as possible, and she will be as loyal as any dog. Give her a permanent grazing companion – her own calf (but watch for suckling problems), a young heifer, a donkey – anything for companionship, but preferably bovine so that she can express her natural affections (she will wash you, too, but it can be too vigorous a gesture) and sexuality.

Finally, is a house cow profitable? Properly managed, she should at least break even in financial terms, that is, her produce should compensate for any expenditure. Shop milk and other dairy produce become increasingly expensive and bland. In addition to milk, your cow can also give you calves to sell or to raise as beef for your family's consumption, and she can be used as a workhorse for a few hours a day if you are reasonable and feed her properly.

But she will give you far more than financial profit. If she is the right cow, and you are the right person, you will reap a rich harvest of satisfaction.

2 Which Cow?

There is nothing wrong with a mongrel house cow. Part of the fun is experimenting with breed crossing to produce the ideal animal. The pure breeds have specific characteristics which affect productivity, temperament and price as well as appearance, and these brief outlines of a selection of breeds might help you make your choice. They are listed in size order, starting with the smallest – and the smaller they are the less food they need. The higher the 'average butter fat per cent', the more cream (and butter) you get.

Dexter
Very small cow with short legs; usually black, but can be red or dun. The homesteader's standby in the past. Very economical and hardy; can live on the roughest grazing and still produce excellent ratio of milk to food intake. Dual-purpose breed: calves good for beef, giving small, lean joints at about two or two-and-a-half years old. Needs good fencing, but ideal for tethering if trained. Av weight 650lb. Av yield 500–700gal pa. Av butter fat 4.2 per cent.

Jersey
Dainty, beautiful eyes, lovely temperament (I admit my bias). Colours vary from smoky grey through familiar golden tan to almost black, occasionally with white patches, and with characteristic broad, pale muzzle. Hardy, light-footed on the land. Needs good quality grazing and hay but appetite will not overwhelm you. Creamy 'gold top' milk, the best for butter-making. But no butcher buys a Jersey or Jersey cross for beef: the meat tastes fine but the fat is too yellow for the customer. Very easy calvers with a wide pelvis; excellent mothers and foster mothers. Long productive life.
Av weight 850lb. Av yield 700–900gal pa. Av butter fat 5.0 per cent.

WHICH COW?

Guernsey

A Channel Islands breed like the Jersey, with all its advantages but not such a pretty face. Bred for its characteristically rich yellow milk, excellent for cream. Bigger than a Jersey so it eats more and has higher yields. Colour usually golden brown with white patches, sandy eyelashes, amber hooves. Bull calves a little more acceptable to the butcher.
Av weight 1,000lb. Av yield 800–1,000gal pa. Av butter fat 4.8 per cent.

Ayrshire

A pretty cow and a good house cow: milk *and* beef. Typical wedge shape of dairy animal. Various shades of brown with white. Hardy, healthy and adaptable; makes good use of less-than-best grazing. Udder very sound and sturdy, medium-size teats, easy to milk; quiet temperament. Good cream.
Av weight 1,150lb. Av yield 1,100–1,200gal pa. Av butter fat 4.0 per cent.

Dairy Shorthorn

A workmanlike cow. Dual-purpose breed, good for milk and lean beef. Roan, red, red and white. Strong, hardy and adaptable; good suckler. Usually a herd animal rather than a house cow. Breed society keen to promote the dairy-type animal.
Av weight 1,200lb. Av yield 900–1,000gal pa. Av butter fat 3.6 per cent.

Friesian

The common black and white: 85 per cent of Britain's milk and 70 per cent of home-killed beef come from Friesian herds. Pedigree animals must have four white socks and white tail switch. Large and (a personal opinion) rather boring, but very practical dual-purpose breed. Eats a lot of anything; yields a lot of mundane milk. Ideal for the farmer, perhaps less so for the smallholder, but large teats give you something to grab hold of.
Av weight 1,550lb. Av yield 1,200gal pa. Av butter fat 3.7 per cent.

Welsh Black

Dual-purpose, primarily beef but ideal sucklers and good house cows. Very hardy and weatherproof hill breed, with heavy body, and thick black coat which is long and rust-tinged in winter. Excellent and protective mothers; good foragers; long and even lactation with less of a marked flush of milk after calving. Will eat anything.

Av weight 1,350–1,700lb. Av yield 700–900gal pa. Av butter fat 4.0 per cent.

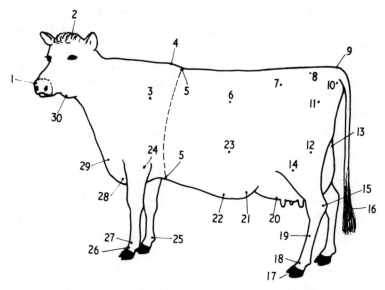

Fig 1 Parts of the body of a dairy cow:
1 muzzle 2 poll 3 shoulder blade 4 withers 5 girth 6 ribs 7 hip 8 plate 9 tail head 10 pin bones 11 thurl 12 thigh 13 escutcheon 14 stifle 15 hock 16 switch 17 cleats 18 fetlock 19 shank 20 udder 21 milk veins 22 milk well 23 barrel 24 elbow 25 dew claw 26 coronet 27 pastern 28 brisket 29 dewlap 30 throat

Having selected your breed, write to the relevant breed society for as much information as they can give you (the addresses are in the Appendix, p. 101). The society will be able to tell you points to look for when choosing your cow. Better still, be on excellent terms with a farmer specialising in the breed you have chosen, but use him only to advise you: do not buy from him. Buying from a friend is asking for trouble – you have no comeback.

Check your local paper and *Farmers Weekly* for private sales of stock, preferably in small numbers. Leave the big dispersal sales and markets to the experts. Ask everyone and anyone if they know of a farmer wanting to dispose of older cows no longer viable in a modern dairy herd but quite adequate as house cows. You will not be demanding such high yields as a dairy farmer: he will often be happy to sell a cow whose maximum daily yield is only, say, three or four gallons, or who is difficult to spot when bulling (you, with only a cow or two, will have such a personal interest in her that observation will be much easier, but make sure that she does not have some fertility problem). Occasionally you may be lucky enough to find a house-cow owner who has become disenchanted with the tie-down of regular milking, and obviously an animal already used to hand milking is ideal, though most machine-milked animals take quite happily to hand milking. Ask your vet if he knows of any potential house cows.

First-calf heifers are cheaper but unproven and they can be very jumpy to start with; they are best left to someone with experience. Go for an animal on her second or third calf; she will be about three or four years old with several good milking years ahead of her, and she will have a record you can check of yields, reliability, calvings and so on.

There are some general guidelines, of course. The ideal dairy-type cow is wedge-shaped, that is, she is slim in the head and neck, her back is straight and not swayed, her pelvis is wide for easy calving and her 'barrel' is deep for carrying the calf. A dual-purpose or beef cow will be more rectangular than triangular.

The udder is what it is all about, so check that first. It should hang evenly and firmly and should not be pendulous; its base, or 'sole', should be flat. A large udder does not necessarily mean a heavy milker. After milking, the udder skin at the back should form soft pleats and there should be no hard areas – check for any hardness or inflammation which might indicate mastitis. There should be four teats (freakish examples do occur), which should be of a size you find easy to grasp. Jerseys tend to have rather small back teats, which makes milking them harder work.

Check the feet for lameness and the joints for swelling, especially above the hoof. Check that the cow has adequate teeth

Cow and calf

Dexter: The smallholder's cow. A short-legged mountain breed from South West Ireland. Tough; able to utilise rough grazing efficiently

Jersey: Doe eyes and pale muzzle give the Jersey a pretty face. Centuries of tether-grazing on the island of Jersey have produced a docile breed ideal as a house cow: the best for cream

to eat with: there are no upper front teeth, and the important ones are the large grinding molars top and bottom which pulp roughage. Check the eyes for New Forest disease (see Chapter 6). Watch out for undue nervousness, remembering that most cows will back away from humans, particularly if they are wearing white like a vet. Watch the cow in the parlour during a normal milking routine and avoid her if she is difficult to handle, or fidgety, or fussy with her food. Do not buy if she is a habitual kicker: the spitefulness is probably deep-seated.

If you are buying from a dairy farmer, he might well have official Milk Marketing Board (MMB) records of each individual cow, giving her yields for each lactation, details of butter fat and protein content of her milk, calving dates and calf sexes. Have a look at these records and at the pedigree or registration certificate if there is one.

A healthy cow has bright eyes and looks alert and interested; she has thin, elastic skin with a bloom to it; she likes her food and comes willingly into the parlour (though a bad stockman can make any cow reluctant). A cow chewing her cud and belching is healthy and contented.

If the records are in order, and she looks sound, and you like her face and your adviser agrees, it might still be worth asking your vet to give her a final checkover before you sign the cheque. Ask him to ensure that the herd is 'accredited', that is, free from brucellosis (which the Ministry of Agriculture – MAFF – is trying to eradicate) and that the tuberculin tests are clear. It is as well to be on good terms with the Ministry from the start: you may not legally move any animal anywhere without the written permission of your District Veterinary Officer (DVO), and buying from an unaccredited herd can cause endless and tedious problems. The procedure is detailed in the Appendix, p. 103. On first acquaintance with you, the Ministry will take a legitimate interest in the accommodation you are offering the cow: representatives will come and check it out and at the same time assure themselves that there are at least two fences between your cow and any neighbouring cattle. Red tape, though necessary, is the bane of the farmer's life.

Before you take your irrevocable decision, remember how

important it is that you should actually like the cow. You will be milking her twice a day, and it can at times be a trying experience. If you do not even like the animal it will be a nightmare. Friendliness is important, of course. But do not treat a cow like a dog: if you stick out your hand she will jump away. A cow's eye is something like a fly's, and approaching objects seem to enlarge very suddenly. Always let a cow come to you; offer her a whole, solid body to sniff rather than a fist. If she is curious enough to approach you as you stand quietly, she is basically friendly.

To get the cow from the farm to your field might present the odd problem. The simplest answer is to pay a cattle transporter to do it for you, but you will probably find that his smallest container can carry twenty cows and it does seem a waste of space. He will, of course, charge accordingly. Make sure that you have adequate access for his monstrous vehicle to unload: if the lorry can back right up to the field gateway or the cowshed door, there is no problem.

If you are transporting the cow yourself in your own trailer or a borrowed horsebox, make sure your insurance covers the occasion. Put ample barley straw on the floor (barley straw provides fodder as well as bedding and it will give the cow something to do on the journey) and provide drinking water for a trip of any length. The seller should know enough about his animal to load her, but if not you will need a rope halter of the type which tightens around the nose and a bucket of cattle cake which can be rattled as an inducement. Hay in a hay net helps as a lure, too. The cow will not much like the idea of entering an unknown confined space; be gentle but firm and remember that cows often follow out of curiosity better than when driven or halter-led. Cover the ramp with straw and let her find her footing in her own time: ramps can be slippery when an animal is used to the firmness of a field. If she is reluctant, help by placing her forefeet on the ramp.

If lures and friendly persuasion do not work, there are ways of moving a reluctant cow. If you are using a rope halter, at all costs keep her head up. If she gets her head down (and she will try it) the next thing you know she has burst free of your grip, or she is lying down in protest and only a full blast of water from a hosepipe will get her up again. And then she will be in a state of panic. You will find your strength is greater if you pass the leading rope behind your back and lean on it, but never wrap the rope round your hand or you will be in trouble. You can keep her head up by inserting your fingers into her nostrils and leading her by the nose. A stubborn cow does better on the halter if you stand beside her and, while pulling forwards with the halter rope, use the other hand to slap her rump or to pinch the base of her tail; or you can take hold of the tail itself and use it as a second rope.

If you really must, twist her tail. Grasp the tail about halfway down and curl it gradually in a flat circle against her buttocks. As you do so you put pressure on the root of the tail and this usually persuades a cow forwards.

Assistants can be a help or a hindrance – the more people, the more nervous the cow, but they can make a human fence for you. Two people can lock hands behind the cow and heave her forward.

When you unload after the journey, leave her alone to recover her composure. See that she has ample water and grazing or fodder, and let her take her time getting to know her new surroundings before you force yourself upon her. When it is time for her to get to know you, keep your movements slow and quiet, talk to her constantly, and above all be patient. It has been said that the ideal cowman is a self-confident introvert. Do not be ashamed of talking to your cow; it is important that she should recognise your voice, and one of your first tasks will be to persuade her to come at your call. Decide on a consistent call sign – be it 'Come up', 'Coo-ee', 'Cow-ow' or whatever inane sound you like – then teach it to her by associating the call with food lures. There is nothing more exasperating than being ignored by your own cow when you try to call her up from the farthest corner of the pasture at milking time when it is raining and you have to plod out there and round her up.

3 Accommodation

The Field

The ideal field has well established but 'clean' pasture with mixed grasses and herbs but no thistles; it is soundly hedged or walled, with shelter-belts here and there and perhaps a small copse to provide leaves in the diet and shelter. Above all, it offers variety. It needs good drainage (poorly drained land encourages parasitic worms). It contains a simple field shelter to provide a dry bed in very bad weather, and has a constant source of fresh water either from a mains supply or from a running stream through a pond.

Ideals are hard to come by but they can still be pursued. Take a section of another man's field of stubble: here is how to turn that into a home for a cow.

Fencing

The area needs boundaries. If there are no cattleproof hedges or walls, you must fence. Cows can jump, particularly youngsters and particularly if they are 'gadding' in the summer, when gadflies cause them to race around the field with their tails in the air.

There are really only two economical methods of fencing, if you exclude post and rails as being expensive or laborious. Electric fencing is the simplest, most adaptable and cheapest, but it has a temporary air and does not state to the world 'This is *my* field!' Barbed-wire does: it is the sign of a bad farmer (a good one has proper hedges), but in the beginning you may have little option.

1 Barbed-wire. To erect a sound barbed-wire fence you need strength, assistance and know-how, but once up it should need no further attention for ten years or so. You will need: split chestnut stakes with 4in butts, about 6ft long; straining posts at intervals of about every 50 yards in the length of the fence – chestnut again,

some 5–6in in diameter and 7ft 6in long; struts, 8ft long, which are wedged against the straining posts along the line of the wire to fortify them; three strands of galvanised double barbed-wire; some form of gate, or rails sliding through U-bolts. You will need to borrow some basic tools if you are doing the job yourself: a mall (a wooden beetle with a large barrel-shaped head) for knocking in the posts without splitting them; a pointed length of metal, such as an old buckrake tine, for stabbing into the ground to start the post-holes if you do not have access to a proper post-hole borer; a trenching spade for digging in the straining posts and struts, and a tamp (use a sledge-hammer) for firming up; a wire strainer to tighten the barbed-wire; large galvanised staples to hold the wire to the posts; and a hammer.

The posts will last longer if they are peeled of bark and at least the sunken parts creosoted. Point the tips before driving the posts, and do the job in spring when the ground is still reasonably soft.

First erect your straining posts and struts. Dig a hole 3ft deep for each post, drop in the post and fill in with rubble and earth, tamping vigorously as you do so and checking that the post is straight. It must be very firm: it will be taking a considerable strain from the wire. Make notches on the two sides of the straining post along the line of the wire to receive the struts, and shape the top of the struts to fit the notches snugly. The top of the strut should be at a height of about 3ft 6in from ground level. Sink the base of the strut by digging out a 'rabbit hole', but try to leave a block of untouched subsoil to act as a rampart for the foot of the strut. If the fit is not quite tight, ram in some rubble or chunks of offcuts (elm does not rot in moisture) at the foot of the strut. Knock the top of the strut sideways into the notch with the sledge-hammer. The fit will tighten up when the wire is strained into position.

Now place the split posts roughly in position: they should be about 9ft apart. The barbed-wire will be stapled to the inside face of each post so that any pressure from an animal in the field forces the wire against the post. Keep the line dead straight between straining posts: curved fences are useless and impossible for straining the wire.

Make a start on the post-holes by driving in the buckrake tine until it has made a hole some 18in deep and just wide enough to take the post. Then knock the post in with the mall. Do not use a metal-headed sledge-hammer or the post will split and splay. Check that the posts stay vertical as you drive them in; in particular make sure that they do not lean into or away from the line of the wire. It helps to have someone holding the posts in position.

Please, try to avoid using living trees as fencing posts! The wire cuts into the tree and over the years the tree grows over the wire. This ruins the tree's potential value as veneer, should it be oak for example, and it also creates a nasty hazard for a future generation's chainsaw.

Now for the skilled part: it is as well to have an experienced helper to strain the wire. If the wire is left slack, any cow with an adventurous spirit will get through. Make it tighter than you dare, but beware! If you strain the wire beyond its tensile capacity it will snap and whiplash across the field. Anyone within range can receive a nasty wound. That is why you should ask the help of an experienced fencer, who will be able to judge the correct amount of tension. Wear heavy leather gloves, too. The danger of whiplash is lessened if you staple the wire loosely to each post, or alternate posts, as you go along.

To strain wire, use proper wire strainers, though a skilled man can 'claw' it round the post with two hammers. Each type of strainer has its own character and each defies any description of use. If you are turning any angle, however slight, put in a temporary post along the line of the wire to strain on to.

The wires should be at heights from the ground of, say, 3ft 3in, 2ft, and 9in. The bottom wire is dispensable if you have no young stock, though cows are quite capable of kneeling down and shrugging themselves under if there are only two strands of wire. To unroll a reel of barbed-wire, slip a strong stick or pipe through the reel and let it unroll itself as you walk along, preferably one person on each side. Never be persuaded into buying cheap wire: it does not pay. Nor is single-strand wire strong enough for the job.

When the wire is acceptably tight, staple it firmly to each post. Do not drive the staples right in: the wire needs to 'breathe' with changes in temperature, and anyway tight stapling will in due course cut into the wire and introduce rust. Place the staples at an angle to the grain of the wood to avoid splitting along the grain.

Try to avoid climbing your wire: weight will slacken it. Build a stile if there is any point where climbing is necessary, or protect the barbs with a piece of rubber tyre or plastic fertiliser bags, which your young stock will probably try to eat.

To buy new gates will cost you a fortune. Make sure your gateway is wide enough for a tractor and implements – some balers and tedders are pretty wide so allow 10ft or even 12ft to be safe. Buy four U-bolts (or D-bolts) which are squared-off U-shaped irons with pointed ends which can simply be hammered into the gate posts. Acquire two lengths of timber for gate rails: old, well-seasoned but sound rafters (4 × 2in) from a demolition site are very adequate but will need creosoting. I have used larch poles, but they can be whippy and might need an additional centre post to support them. The post can be set into a concrete sleeve so that it can easily be lifted out to allow tractor access through the gateway. Drill large holes at either end of the slip rails and into the gate posts so that you can insert coach bolts or large nails to anchor the rails: cows love to put their heads between the rails and scratch their necks, which can easily dislodge everything.

2 Electric Fencing. Whereas barbed-wire has an air of permanency, electric fencing requires much less heavy labour and capital. You will need only one strand of wire (but two if you have young stock) at a height of about 2ft 6in or 3ft. The posts can be lighter in all proportions and need be only 2in hazel or larch poles sunk 12–18in and furnished with special nail-on insulators available at any farm supply store. The posts can be placed 10 or 12yd (yes, *yards*) apart. You need firmer posts for the corners, to take the wire strain, though electric wire is nothing like as tensed as barbed-wire. Ordinary chestnut splits could do the corner job, dug in with rubble or malleted to a depth of 18in and strutted. Alternatively, you can buy metal 'pigtail' posts, already insulated, with tripod posts for the corners. These are ideal for temporary fences: they are easily stamped into the ground and as easily removed.

Make sure that all points of contact with the wire are insulated. Some people save on insulators by using baler twine, but it must be the plastic sort.

There are two types of electric wire: stranded galvanised or the newer 'polywire' which has fine copper and polypropylene strands twisted together. The latter is cheaper, clean, light, visible, very manageable and easily cut and tied, but some people feel it does not carry the current as well as the ordinary wire, nor join together with sufficient contact. In due course the copper filaments tend to break so it is not as long-lasting as galvanised wire.

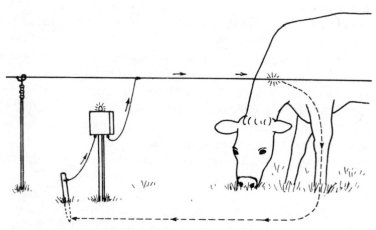

Fig 2 Electric fencing circuit: when an animal touches the electrified conductor wire, the current from the fencing unit passes through the body and is earthed into the ground, completing the electrical circuit and giving the animal an uncomfortable shock.

The wire does not, by the way, need to form a complete circuit. The completion of the electric circuit is through the animal: when it touches the wire the pulse of current is earthed through its body to the ground, thus giving it the shock required to dissuade it from barging through. It is a good idea to use plastic twine at one or both ends of a straight stretch of wire because it makes the straining of it much easier. Wire expands and contracts according to the weather and will need retightening on hot days: slack wire gives an ineffectual shock.

Grass is a conductor. If it is in contact with the wire it tends to short the electricity down into the ground and drain your batteries, so keep all growth clear of the wire. Watch out after wind or rain, which may bend long grasses into contact with the wire although when straight they seem well away from it. But any sensible cow will do this trimming for you if there is only one strand.

The fencer itself is the most expensive item you will need. The price of a new one will make you think twice, so choose carefully. Transistorised fencers are more expensive but the cost of their batteries is much lower. The batteries last about four or five months on average in regular use. The dry 6-volt batteries needed for other types of fencer cost three times as much as those for transistorised fencers but they are rechargeable. These types of fencer weigh a great deal more but on the other hand they are more likely to be found at farm sales. If you feel rich you can choose a mains-operated fencer but you need an accessible mains supply.

The fencer must have an earthing rod plunged into the ground and it should be noted that the efficiency of the unit will be impaired if the ground is too dry, so sink the rod well in. Some units combine the earthing rod with the stand for the fencer.

Now connect the unit to the wire, usually with an integral crocodile clip, then switch on and test. You can either buy a special tester, or you can touch the wire with your finger. Although the shock is merely unpleasant, some of the bravest men will not touch a live wire; instead, they take a blade of grass and use that as an extension of their fingers, reducing the shock to a tingle. Alternatively, they take a metal pigtail post, holding it by the insulated part, and see if the metal section sets off a spark from the wire.

Several fencers give you a choice of 'high' or 'normal' shock. The higher setting is used for training stock but will not normally be needed otherwise. Training is essential. Place some appealing hay or green stuff on the wire and switch on high: one taste, and most animals in future avoid a wire, even when it is not switched on and, in some cases, when replaced by a harmless substitute. My cow respects an innocent line of string. An advantage of the older type of fencer is its loud ticking; the animal soon connects the sound with the shock. Transistorised fencers are virtually silent, with a flashing light not easily visible in daylight. Put up warning signs if members of the public are likely to blunder into the wire.

When you dismantle an electric fence, take care to reel up the wire as you go, however laborious the chore. There is nothing more exasperating than tangled wire.

3 Tethering. Tether grazing is the cheapest and most versatile 'containment' of all, but it requires a docile animal, early training, a portable source of fresh water, and constant monitoring. You can use a leather head harness with a strongly attached ring underneath, or a stout leather collar. The length of the tether chain is a commonsense matter depending on how often you are prepared to shift the animal (probably two or three times a day): 20ft is a manageable length. Solder a firm spring clip on to one end of the chain to hook on to the harness ring. On the other end solder a larger ring to slip on to the tethering post, which can be a flat-headed iron stake or crowbar firmly sledge-hammered into the ground at each shift, or you can try patented corkscrew tethering posts for guard dogs though these are nothing like strong enough for an adventurous cow. The chain ring allows swivel on the stake and avoids coiling or entanglement. For a really headstrong animal you could get a bull tether but it will cost you more than barbed-wire fencing for a four-acre field. Have a look around farm sales: there is always a splendid variety of ironmongery which, with a little imagination, will come in useful. Hoard chains: they have many uses.

Grass
Cows live on grass, and the establishment of good pasture must be a priority. If the field is stubble, do not plough it. Grass needs a firm bed. Go over the stubble time and time again with harrows – first discs and then chains. Do the job thoroughly: as a smallholder you will probably want a long-term ley so it must last a while. Avoid wet weather for this work.

However much it is against your principles and pocket, it is wise to apply fertiliser as you prepare the ground since it will not yet have received the natural stuff from your cow: 1–2cwt per acre will get it off to a good start. Use nitrogen for quick growth, or compounds for sustained growth, but if you are using only nitrogen remember that the ground also needs phosphates and potash. Also, some say that the quick growth produced by nitrogen is less rich in protein, since the grass can outgrow its own strength.

There are many varieties of grass. Ask your local seed merchant or MAFF adviser to recommend a mixture suited to local conditions and soil. Timothy is good if you want to make hay as well as grazing; Italian rye gives you an early bite in spring; perennial rye is a staple ingredient; a little white clover fixes nitrogen and cuts down on fertiliser bills, but too much clover causes bloat in cows and clover takes over the whole field in drought situations. Herbs give the cow variety – try burnet, chicory, or sheep's parsley, at about 1lb to the acre. You will probably need about 30lb grass seed per acre.

Sow the grass in April or September, on a dry, windless day with a promise of light rain and warmth in a day or so. Heavy rain will wash your seed and fertiliser straight into the ditches. Tell the pigeons to go elsewhere for a while, though most grass seed is treated against such predators.

April-sown grass should not really be grazed until the following spring; it is probably more practical to sow in September and graze lightly from May onwards. If you have an electric fencer, you can fence off part of the field for hay, but give it a good chance to recover after haymaking before you graze it. It will need another boost of fertiliser as it will not have had stock on it giving natural manure, and you will still see the difference between the grazed and the haymaking areas next year.

If the grazing area grows too fast for the cow, top it back to about 4–6in before it goes to flower and grows too coarse to be palatable. Topping stimulates fresh growth and keeps the pasture green. Watch out for larks' nests.

If your stocking rate is right and you control grazing sensibly, there is very little else you need to do to grazed grass. Give it a rest every now and then if you can; keep it topped if the cow does not;

attack thistles vehemently and never let them go to seed; keep the field and its borders clear of poisonous plants such as bracken, mare's tail, yew and ragwort; let the bugs and rooks disperse the cowpats. In wet weather watch out for 'poaching' (that is, trampling the grass into a quagmire) though a single animal should not have much effect on the field until heavy autumn rains set in when, if you are on heavy land in particular, it is wise to put her indoors anyway. The cow can take the weather, but the field cannot.

Spring grass is rich in protein but as the season ages so does the grass. Its fibre content and bulk increase but its goodness decreases. Be careful with the autumn flush of grass growth: the cow will get nice and full, and probably fat, but she will not make much milk on it. Be very careful with spring grass and introduce the cow gradually to grazing or she will bloat suddenly and you will have problems.

The quality of hay depends on the quality of grass. If you make hay early, say in late May, it will be of very high quality but there will not be much of it. If you make it late, say the end of July, you will have plenty but the quality is less. Haymaking is truly an art, and requires luck as well. Get experience with someone else's hay before you tackle your own: like milking, it cannot be taught, it has to be practised. You need at least three consecutive sunny days to make a good job of it.

Cut your hay mechanically or, if you are skilled, with a scythe, and let it drop into swathes. Leave it a few hours, then fluff it up into windrows, either mechanically with a cockpheasant, acrobat rake or tedder, or manually (and more effectively) with a wooden hay rake or pitchfork. The aim is to dry the mown hay as quickly as possible to preserve maximum goodness, but if it is handled too vigorously you risk shattering all the good leafy parts: strike a balance. Turn it perhaps twice a day: you want the sun to get at every blade and stem and seedhead. It should grow paler as time goes by but should still retain a hint of its colour; it should smell sweet.

If hay is stored too moist, it will go musty and mouldy and your cow will throw it all over the place rather than eat it. If it is too sun-dried it may lose some goodness, but it is better than too moist. If you are storing the hay in bales you should reduce the moisture content to 22 per cent (27 per cent if loose) to avoid overheating in the stack.

The moment it is ready, get it baled by a contractor if you can (though as usual the smaller your area the harder and more expensive it is to find a willing man and machine) and get the bales stooked into small groups to breathe a bit before you stack them under cover. Baled hay needs air. If rain threatens, get the hay under cover but try and spread the bales out again in the sun as soon as possible. Store in a dry, airy barn with no rising damp, or make a stack in the open with an airflow underneath and cover the top with agricultural black polythene held in place with string netting or old tyres.

To load a trailer with bales, always make sure that the bottom layers are widest or you will lose the lot at the first corner; stack so that the structure is interlocking. Bales are much easier to handle, both for storing and for use in winter, but if you cannot get hold of a baler store the hay loose. It keeps well but watch out for overheating and spontaneous combustion, especially if the moisture content is too high. The danger period is the first two months: keep a check on the temperature at the heart of the stack. 140°F (60°C) is a warning level. At 160°F (71°C) call the fire brigade.

It is possible to handmake bales with a little ingenuity but it is very difficult to pack them tight and they tend to disintegrate on handling.

A ton of good hay might see one cow through a short winter but always store too much. The price of hay rockets in a cold wet spring.

If those sunny drying days never come, make silage instead. Silage is the farmer's standby. It is a method of preserving summer grass when haymaking is difficult, and it is a rich nutrient: highest quality silage can be used to replace concentrates in the milk-production ration. Its disadvantages are bulk and smell, and for the small-time farmer the cost of employing a contractor to make small amounts of silage would be ridiculous. Its advantages are that it makes better productive use of grass than haymaking – 4 tons of grass should produce 3 tons of silage of the same dry-matter content, and allowing for further loss in store from moulds, etc, the loss is still only half that involved in haymaking.

The farm method of silage-making involves special machinery to cut, chop, wilt, bruise and mince up the crop (you can make silage from anything green, for example, maize, marrowstem kale, green oats, sugarbeet or turnip tops, and sunflowers, as well as from grass, clover and lucerne). The farmer will then pile it all into a specially built pit covering a considerable area, squash it really flat with a tractor to consolidate it, and cover with a tarpaulin or black plastic sheeting held down with old tyres. The aim is to exclude all air. Many farmers use additives to ensure proper ensilaging.

If this sounds like an overgrown compost heap, it almost is, but with a vital difference: that exclusion of air. Let air into your silage and everything decomposes into inedibility.

It is possible to make small quantities of silage for one or two cows, and although you may not believe it when you see and smell the stuff, cows adore it. It makes a change from hay all winter long. Get some *undamaged* strong plastic bags (old fertiliser bags are fine if thoroughly cleaned out). Cut your grass and leave it to wilt in the sun for a day. Your aim is to reduce the moisture level to 30 per cent dry matter/70 per cent moisture. Too high a moisture content means too little sugar for fermentation.

Now pack the wilted grass very tightly into the bags and seal the tops to make sure everything is airtight. Then just leave it alone until you need to use it in winter.

If the grass is very wet you need to add molasses to help fermentation. You can use grass mowings for silage provided there is no trace of oil from the mower and, of course, no weedkiller. Your local council might be a source of grass, or the sportsfield, but make sure the grass does not contain plants which remain poisonous after cutting and preserving (see Appendix, p 111).

Silage-making can start by mid-May if growth is sufficient and, if you are prepared to use nitrogen heavily on the aftermath, you will be able to take two or three cuts for silage off the same area in a season.

32

Shelter

If your field has no natural shelter in the form of a copse or large trees, build something. You do not usually need planning permission to erect an open-fronted field shelter on agricultural land, and something simple will supply protection from heavy rain and winds and provide a dry place to lie if the cow wants it. A calf *must* have a dry bed: wind and rain together are a calf's worst enemies.

For one cow, a shelter 10 × 8ft is more than adequate in the field. Obviously the open side should be protected from prevailing weather. A cow does not mind rain – in fact she welcomes it as a shower bath – but she hates rain driven into her face by wind. The choice of materials for the shelter is endless and depends on local availability, ingenuity and your pocket. How about faggots – the bunches of birch brushwood used for racecourse jumps – or wattle, made from hazel thinnings? Another cheap idea is timber-yard offcuts, the pieces left after a round tree trunk is squared up before being sawn into planks. Wany elm is currently one of the cheapest sawn claddings; it should not need creosoting and should be in plentiful supply. Do not nail too close to the edges or it will split, and it needs firm pinning to avoid warping. Fertiliser bags can be used if you are really desperate and do not object to the sight of them, though young stock and the occasional cow tend to eat them with dire consequences. On the whole, natural materials look best in the field. Straw bales are possible but need the protection of chicken wire to avoid their being eaten and they need a firm framework inside and out to prevent dislodging. The roof is the most important part: if the structure is large enough and well sited you might not need any cladding at all on the sides. Spend money on the uprights and the roof. The latter can be, for example, galvanised tin, corrugated tin, the more manageable lightweight corrugated perspex, floorboards covered with roofing felt or creosoted and battened to avoid leaks – the list is endless. Uncorrugated tin is prone to leak at the seams even when overlapped, and it is difficult to handle until you are used to it. To get a galvanised roofing nail through tin, place the sheet on a very firm and solid surface and punch a hole with a centre punch before driving in the nail.

Water

The only other furniture you will need in the field is a source of fresh water. A lactating cow will drink a dozen gallons a day, more in very hot weather or if her yield is high, and it is essential that she has as much as she wants. Water makes milk, apart from keeping her healthy. Natural ponds with springs keeping them fresh are lovely but can get very boggy: make a concrete ramp for access, going right into the pond. The easier water supply is from the mains into a galvanised or plastic tank (though some cows do not like drinking from plastic) or an old bath tub, with a ballcock to regulate the flow, but unless the supply is already laid on to the field it might cost a lot. You can, local by-laws permitting, run a very long hose from your garden tap to a galvanised container and keep filling it up as needed, but cold weather can ice up the hose and then you are reduced to buckets. Heavy-duty agricultural polythene piping is better than a garden hose but can still freeze up unless it is buried or clad along its length.

Provide a mineral salt lick near the water supply: cows love them and they make up for any possible deficiencies in the natural mineral content of your land.

Winter-quarters

You will need a sound structure to house the cow in the worst of the winter weather, where she can also calve if necessary and where you can milk when the weather deters you from milking in the field. Open-air milking is much healthier for both of you but if it is pouring with rain it is very uncomfortable and the milk gets diluted. You could milk in the field shelter but it is best to have a concrete or paved floor, which can be kept clean and which gives respite from mud for both your feet and the cow's. Give the concrete a slightly rough finish so that it does not get slippery in icy weather. I milk in the field, where I have created a holding paddock at the gateway, with an area of heavy paving slabs for milking. It is useful for visits by the vet: my cow Rosie is familiar with the area and is less agitated out of doors than restricted inside for such visits.

In winter, particularly on heavy land, it will be best for the field

Guernsey: The 'golden' cow: a golden pigment to the coat, and golden Guernsey milk. As manageable as a Jersey, with higher average yields

Ayrshire: A stylish and adaptable cow from South-West Scotland. Strong udder, high-protein milk with a good cream line

Dairy Shorthorn: A practical cow, developed from the old Teeswater cattle. Bred to produce both milk and meat.

Charolais: A large beef animal from central France. Carefully selected bulls are crossed with dairy breeds to give a beefier calf

and the cow if she is housed at night, if not during the day as well. For full-time confinement she needs *space*, though in the old days dairy cows were kept chained to their mangers for months on end without apparent ill effect. That is quite unnatural: cows need exercise and variety as much as any creature, though they are said to give more milk if restricted in this way because they are not 'wasting' energy on movement.

The ideal winter-quarters include an enclosed, roofed area at least 10 × 15ft and a concreted yard for sun, air and exercise. The concrete, incidentally, will keep the cow's hooves in good trim.

Unless you know what you are doing, do not try to build the winter-quarters yourself. Try to obtain the use of a suitable existing barn or stable, perhaps in exchange for milk. Building your own cowhouse will be your largest capital outlay, costing far more than the cow herself.

The enclosed area must be well ventilated but draughtfree, with as much natural light as possible. I use an antique open-fronted cartshed with a very high gable and a rammed earth floor, which needs a fair amount of bedding straw but which is otherwise ideal.

The equipment you will need within the cowhouse includes:

Fresh drinking water (as in the field), preferably from an insulated tank rather than straight from the mains.

Hay rack or nets. Racks can be the built-in wooden variety, or can be improvised from rigid wire mesh or hazel rods. Hay nets should be large, strong and tarred.

Salt lick in a metal holder near the water.

Broad-based feed bowl or secured bucket for concentrates, or built-in manger. A floor-level manger can be tiled for easy cleaning, but make sure that at that level it is accessible only to the front end of the cow!

Neck chain, to keep her in place when necessary, secured to a manger ring.

Source of illumination: a battery-powered lantern is safest, hung on a high nail.

Pitchfork and barrow for mucking out.

Bedding material.

Straw is the usual bedding, but in some years its price rockets due to a shortage of hay and it has been treated as fodder rather than bedding. Wheat straw is best for bedding, as barley straw tends to be eaten. There are alternatives to straw. Sawdust in a 9in layer is warm and absorbent, but you have to remove dung regularly, and you must be sure that the sawn wood had not been treated with arsenic-based preservatives. You can use woodshavings (not chippings); wood fibre, for example, bark specially macerated and sold commercially as bedding – but watch out for large splinters; shredded newspaper, so long as you have an efficient base layer for drainage; peat in a 9in layer (2in for calves) on a good drainage layer; spent mushroom compost (peat-based rather than manure-based); or you can buy 'cow mats' but these are only useful if you have made a special bedding cubicle.

The basic foundation floor can be bare earth (preferably chalk or sandy soils for good drainage: clay can be rammed solid but must then be drained as if it was concrete); concrete, properly sloped and channelled for drainage; or hardcore, well rammed to avoid loose stones causing foot problems. Next comes a base layer of deep sand (avoiding abrasive types), ground limestone, chalk (avoid flints), 'fly' ash from the local power station, straw bales laid out like a parquet floor with the strings removed, bundles of non-thorn hedge or forestry trimmings about a foot deep, bracken cut *brown* (it retains poisonous properties cut green), or old woven hurdles.

There are two ways of dealing with manure. You can clear out all the bedding whenever it needs it, or you can just keep adding clean bedding on top and clear out very occasionally. The latter method works better if you make the effort to remove dung daily; its advantage is that it builds up a lovely warm barrier between the cow and the ground, and its disadvantage is the Herculean labour of the eventual clear-out, especially if you are using a fork and barrow rather than a tractor.

For milking, you will need further equipment:

Stainless-steel milk bucket (only stainless steel can be kept immaculately hygienic, though it is noisy material; some modern plastics will withstand boiling water).

Three-legged milking stool – more manoeuvrable than an upended log. Make sure it is low enough to avoid backache. Experts dispense with a stool and squat on their haunches.

Bucket for udder washing (buckets are always useful – have plenty).

Cloth for udder washing, preferably disposable so that it does not get a chance to harbour germs.

Plentiful supply of hot water.

And you will need even more equipment for the dairy – butter churns and the like – but you can acquire these gradually as the need takes you.

4 Food

A house cow will happily survive, and give you reasonable milk, on good pasture in summer and good hay with some grain in the winter – that is, feeding at its most basic, making no allowance for vagaries of climate, lack of good grazing, seasonal deterioration in grass quality, local mineral deficiencies, variety in the diet, the stage of the cow's lactation, or any of the other factors which forever exercise dairy farmers' minds.

A commercial farmer is out to squeeze a maximum yield from his cows at minimum expense. Over the years complex formulas have been evolved to ensure that every morsel of every conceivable food is utilised to its full nutritional potential and that not an ounce is fed unproductively. If your aim is maximum yields combined with maximum profit, purchase a pocket calculator and the MAFF's excellent *Rations for Livestock* (sadly now out of print but you should be able to find a copy secondhand or at your local library) and have a go at comprehending Kellner's starch equivalents (SE) and their relation to Kieldahl's protein equivalents (PE):

SE=[(% digestible crude protein × 0·94) + (%digestible ether extract × 2·41 or 2·12 or 1·91) + (% digestible nitrogen-free extractives) + (% digestible crude fibre) × correction factor

PE=½(% digestible crude protein + % digestible true protein)

The SE and PE of an enormous range of feedstuffs can be found in the MAFF booklet (see Appendix, p 106). Once you know the weight of your cow, the amount of milk she should be giving, and the percentage of butter fat in her milk, you can calculate the total SE and PE requirement of her daily diet and juggle amounts of available food accordingly.

Alternatively, you can try the newer Metabolisable Energy

(ME) system, taking into account the amount of energy produced by the food less the energy required to excrete dung and urine and exhale methane. Energy content of food is measured in megajoules per kilogram of dry matter (MJ/kg DM).

The systems (given in more detail in the Appendix, pp 105–10) are scientific and complex and really irrelevant to a smallholder except as interesting mental exercises. But both systems establish a simple principle which *is* of value to you.

A cow needs a 'maintenance' ration to keep her alive and fit, with enough energy to eat, breathe, defecate, walk about the field and in to milking, and nourish a foetus. On top of this she requires a 'production' ration, which means milk (or meat in the case of a beef animal).

Maintenance
The maintenance ration normally consists of bulky low-protein foods, such as grass, hay, straw, roots, silage and kale. It must contain enough long roughage (high-fibre foods such as grass, hay and straw) to keep the cow's rumen functioning efficiently. You should feed enough, but not so much that she has no appetite left for her production ration: the higher the milk yield, the less the hay.

A dairy cow can be expected to relish $2\frac{1}{2}$–3lb *dry* matter a day for every 100lb liveweight. Summer grass, for example, has 20 per cent dry matter. If the grass is young and growing and at its most nutritional stage (about May) a cow will need nothing but grass to achieve her maintenance ration plus lashings of milk. But the grass grows more slowly and becomes less nutritious as the season wears on, so she will not be getting full value from it. She will probably have enough for maintenance (except during droughts) until after the early autumn flush. Thereafter the maintenance diet will need boosting with hay, or straw if you are pushed, or silage. If you have good stocks, it is probably simplest to feed hay to appetite, but not more than she clears up or you will be throwing away good food.

In winter the maintenance ration comes entirely from preserved grass (hay or silage) and other bulk feeds already mentioned. On no account feed less than 10lb of hay a day or she will have digestive problems. The remainder of the maintenance ration can be calculated from the hay-equivalent table below, remembering to leave room in her appetite for the production ration.

1lb average hay = 3lb medium silage
4lb kale or sugarbeet tops
$4\frac{1}{2}$lb rape
5lb mangels or cabbage
$1\frac{1}{2}$lb oat or barley straw
2lb potatoes
$\frac{1}{2}$lb barley, sugarbeet pulp or concentrate
$2\frac{1}{2}$lb brewers wet grains

A Jersey's daily winter maintenance ration might be:

14lb good hay (or $16\frac{1}{2}$lb average hay)
or 10lb good hay + 26lb mangels

A 10–12cwt cow such as an Ayrshire might get:

18–20lb good hay
or 12lb good hay + 40lb mangels
or 12lb good hay + $4\frac{1}{2}$lb dried sugarbeet pulp
or 10lb good hay + 4lb oat straw + 20lb silage
or 14lb good oat straw + 30lb silage

Production

Next, you want milk, or in the two dry months before calving you need to feed the unborn calf. The production ration normally consists of high-protein concentrates – grains, or cow cake from the mill. It is often more economical to feed enough of the maintenance ration to produce the first gallon of milk (perhaps another 3lb hay + another 4–5lb mangels, cabbage, etc). Then feed higher-protein foods such as crushed barley, crushed oats, maize meal, or proprietary brands of 16 per cent protein dairy cake, at the following rates:

Channel Island breeds: $4\frac{1}{2}$lb per gallon of milk per day
Other breeds: $3\frac{1}{2}$lb per gallon of milk per day

On an energy basis, 1lb barley can be replaced by:

1·0lb standard dairy cake
1·1lb dried sugarbeet pulp (max 8lb Friesian, 6lb Jersey)
1·2lb rolled oats
1·3lb 4-star dried grass (max 8lb Friesian, 6lb Jersey)
6·0lb fresh brewers grains (max 30lb Friesian, 20lb Jersey)
7·5lb kale (max 60lb Friesian, 40lb Jersey)

A Dexter's home-mixed total daily winter rations might be:

10lb silage, kale or roots + 6lb hay and/or barley straw, for maintenance plus the first gallon of milk

Plus production ration after that first gallon of 3lb per gallon of the following mixture:

5cwt rolled barley : 4cwt crushed oats : $\frac{3}{4}$cwt bean or pea meal + $\frac{1}{4}$cwt fish meal for protein : 10lb (*not* cwt) minerals

It is useful to study the standard lactation curve (see Fig 3).

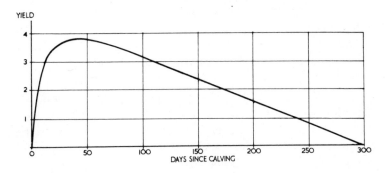

Fig 3 The lactation curve

43

From it you will understand that the milk yield naturally increases rapidly from calving to a peak at between three and six weeks (depending on breed and individual). Thereafter the yield gradually drops at $2\frac{1}{2}$ per cent a week ($1\frac{1}{2}$ per cent for a first-calf heifer) towards the drying-off period about six or eight weeks before calving again if calving is a regular annual event. Any appreciably faster percentage drop means your grass is not as good as you thought, or you are not feeding the right amount, or she is sickening, or it is raining, or she is bulling or pining for her calf. Gear your production ration to take this curve into account. Details of feeding the dry cow prior to calving can be found in Chapter 7.

In addition to these basic rations you must consider the cow's requirements for water, vitamins and minerals, and you should also make her life interesting by giving her variety. Nothing but hay must be very dull, and too much of any one type of food could lead to digestive problems or even mild poisoning. Too much kale, for example, can lead to acetonaemia; too many sugarbeet tops can produce excessive oxalic acid; too much cabbage will taint the milk; too many mangels can cause scouring. Always introduce new foods gradually into the diet.

Cows need vitamins A and D. Vitamin D comes from sunshine and they should get enough from grazing and from hay that grew as grass under at least some sun. Vitamin A is also found in good hay and fresh green forage, but if you are doubtful as to the vitamin supply you can include vitamin additives in the diet.

Minerals depend on what is in your soil and how well the plants can utilise them. Ask your MAFF advisory officer to check the soil and to advise on how to remedy mineral deficiencies or excesses. This is particularly important if you are feeding the cow entirely on home-grown produce. Proprietary cake should contain the necessary balanced minerals. The most important are calcium, phosphorus and salt. Magnesium might be deficient in the spring and autumn grass flushes and can be added at the rate of 2oz a day to the diet. A mineral salt lick near the cow's water supply should provide the basic mineral requirement, or add a home-made mineral mixture to the feed; for example, equal parts of limestone flour or ground chalk with steamed bone flour and common salt, at a rate of 3lb of the mixture in every hundredweight of food.

Fresh water must always be available. Allow up to 15gal a day especially if she is giving a lot of milk or is on dry roughages or the summer is hot and dry.

Finally, here are some notes on different foods and how to feed them. A cow at grass grazes for a while, relaxes to chew the cud for a while, then grazes again, perhaps five times in twenty-four hours. Little and often is natural, though not necessarily convenient for you. Most people feed the production ration at milking time, for convenience and also to encourage let-down of the milk. Buy your concentrates monthly (they do not keep for ever) and store in a dry place – a rubber-lidded dustbin is good for a hundredweight. Never leave stale food in the manger.

Hay
Hay bales weigh anything from 30 to 60lb each so if you are buying pay by the ton, not the bale. Good hay has a memory of green in it; it whispers in the hand and it smells sweet. Break open a bale to make sure it is not full of dust (which will make both you and the cow cough) or mildew. Watch out for dark, mushroomy mould. The cheapest hay is bought 'off the field' at haymaking time. Check *Farmers Weekly* for current average prices. Avoid hay that had heavy rain on it as it lay in the field.

Feed hay in racks: if you just chuck it down at ground level it will be trampled and soiled, which is a waste. Fed ad lib the cow will probably eat about 2lb per hundredweight of bodyweight if she gets nothing else. Make sure the drinking water is in adequate supply: hay is by its nature dry.

Some plants to avoid, whether pasture or in hay, are listed in the Appendix, p 111. These include milk tainters and poisonous plants.

Silage
An 11cwt cow needs a minimum of 45lb silage a day as roughage compared with 12lb hay. Best silage can be used to replace part of the production ration.

Straw

Straw is a bulky fodder and it contains a lot of indigestible fibre. It tends to fill the belly without providing much goodness but its fibrous nature and bulk is of value in preventing bloat and constipation. It is normally used only for store cattle or dry cows and not for valuable milking animals. Some people claim that straw never makes milk. It is usually fed as only part of the roughage ration (never more than 12lb a day to be safe) and is accompanied by protein feeding blocks which help the animal make best use of the straw, or with succulents (turnips, kale, potatoes, etc) to increase palatability. Oat straw is best for feeding, then barley. Wheat straw is of little value and tends to be scratchy. Jerseys will not deign to eat much straw, but Friesians will eat anything.

Greens

Quarter cabbages just before feeding and always feed fresh. Better still, 'fold' the crop, that is, let the cow eat them where they grow, regulating access with a tether or electric fence. They are a good source of protein, and 'make milk', though too much will taint the milk so feed after milking (most taints only last up to four hours). Grow drumheads such as January King, and feed a maximum of 60lb a day. Marrowstem kale is useful from August to the end of December and thousandhead kale stands better in winter: these, too, can be folded or cut and fed in the manger – leaves and stems but not roots. Do not overfeed kale. Two hours' folding will probably feed 60lb. You can also give Brussels sprouts from the garden – feed stems and leaves but not whole sprouts which, fed in excess, lead to anaemia.

Sugarbeet

The leaves are rich in protein, low in fibre, and the crowns supply carbohydrates. Cut and allow to wilt for a week before use to avoid excessive oxalic acid. It can leave a fishy taint in the milk. Dried sugarbeet pulp can be used to replace cereals in the production ration or to replace roots in the maintenance ration. It is a carbohydrate-rich food, bulky and very digestible. Feed up to 8lb and soak before feeding. 1lb dried pulp is the equivalent of 8lb mangels or 1lb crushed oats or 0·9lb barley or 0·8lb maize.

'Molasses' perks the appetite: molassed sugarbeet pulp contains 15–20 per cent sugar.

Other roots and tubers
These are watery carbohydrates and are a poor source of protein. Most cattle love them. Roots contain sugar; potatoes contain starch. Mangels should be lifted and clamped until the new year: if fed straight from the field they will cause scouring. Swedes and turnips are milk tainters. Potatoes should be introduced gradually into the diet and should *never* be fed green or sprouting. Watch out for excessive soil on roots, another cause of scouring. Chop or slice all roots before feeding to avoid choking or bloat. 1lb potatoes is the equivalent of 2lb swedes or mangels, and dairy cows can take a maximum of 20lb potatoes, which are laxative.

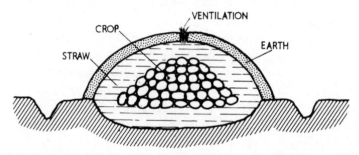

Fig 4 Clamp for storing roots: to keep a root crop safe from winter frosts, dig a shallow pit, line it with straw, heap up the crop (as dry as possible), cover with more straw, and complete with a good firm layer of soil. Allow ventilation by means of a straw 'chimney' projecting through the soil layer.

Grains
Rich in carbohydrates (mainly starch), relatively poor in protein. Crush before feeding to break down the outer coat. Oats and barley are most commonly used; avoid wheat, which is rather glutinous (cows cannot take more than 4–5lb wheat a day without getting indigestion). Maize is a very good milk maker (though more expensive) and is usually fed flaked; it is especially valuable for youngsters.

Bran
This is used as a mild laxative, for which it is made into bran mash with warm water. Fed dry it tends to correct scouring. Balanced feed for milk production but bulky (6lb to the gallon).

Other people's waste
Check locally for what other people throw away or will sell cheap: breweries for brewers grains (high-protein feed, as good as good silage for energy; 6lb = 1lb barley; feed 6lb a day dried grains or up to 25lb wet grains). Starch factories for maize by-products; pea and bean growers for haulms; local growers for carrots and potatoes. Apples can be fed carefully but will give rise to colic.

Supplies
Sources of supply can be a problem on a one-cow scale. Try to find a local arable farmer who will sell you barley by the sackful; buy only a hundredweight at a time because the farmer will probably have better storage and grain-drying facilities than you have. Roll it as you need it, or buy it freshly crushed. If you settle for cake from the mills, they will not like delivering a mere bag or two (it is usually sold in $\frac{1}{2}$cwt or 25kg bags) and you will have to fetch it 'ex mill' or make arrangements with a local dairy farm. The guaranteed nutritional values in mill cake have a limited life, so do not buy in bulk.

Grass
A cow grazes by curling her tongue around the grass, rather than by nibbling it like a horse. She will probably eat about 100lb grass in a day, from which she gets perhaps 20lb dry matter, and she gets maximum benefit from it when it is about 4–6in high, because at this level she neither works too hard to get enough 'bite' nor does she run the risk of eating too much too fast. You can control grazing by using an electric fence or tether: let her graze down an area then close it off for a rest and give her a fresh piece. In this way she has good grass, the grass gets both stimulation and a rest (and natural fertiliser), and if you rest it for long enough you deprive parasitic worms of their livelihood. From the latter point of view you would ideally rotate different

livestock over the grass, because cows' parasites cannot make use of sheep, and vice versa, so the life cycle of the little pests is interrupted.

Be very careful in spring. All cattle look forward to turnout time and the first escape out into the field is an occasion for galloping gleefully, tail high, and legs kicking out wildly – stand clear! Grass is at its lushest and most nutritious, but a cow can easily have too much of a good thing and suffer either from bloat or the staggers (Chapter 6). Introduce grazing gradually: allow only an hour or two each day to start with, feeding hay before she goes to grass to fill her up a bit. Extend the grazing time by degrees, reducing the hay, and add magnesium to her food as a precaution. By mid-May you can let her get on with it. For the house's milk requirements she will not need anything but grass for a month or two, but be sensible and watch both her yield and her body condition, and supplement with cake or grain when you need to. Remember that the value of grass decreases as summer passes by: indeed, some farmers say that grass is only worth grazing for six weeks in the year, but they are pessimists. In summer the grass has a higher dry-matter content than in spring, and although there seems to be less of it, it will in fact satisfy the appetite much more.

Never let your cow get too fat, which is a tendency with house cows because they have no competition for available food, because they are spoilt by their owners, and because more likely than not they are bored. A Jersey should have hollows between hips and ribs on either side, and her ribs should be visible. Any dairy breed is ideally wedge-shaped, or triangular, whether seen from the side or above: you do not want beefy necks and shoulders in dairy animals, whose important points are the udder and a wide pelvis for easy calving. Fit, not fat, is the motto.

5 Milk

In an ideal situation a cow is milked at twelve-hour intervals, but regularity of the hour is more important than the actual time span. Cows appreciate routine. I milk at eight in the morning and six in the evening, give or take the odd hour or two at weekends. A really heavy yielder should be milked three times a day to ease pressure on the udder. If you are prepared to accept less milk than your cow's potential, you can milk only once a day after the first few months if that is more convenient.

No one can teach you how to milk: you have to acquire the knack by practising it. If you have no experience, get some, on someone else's cow. It is not fair on your cow if you ruin her temper and perhaps her udder because you do not know what you are doing. Go to a friendly farmer and practise daily (do not just watch) on a quiet old cow giving about $1\frac{1}{2}$gal a day. If she is giving less than 1gal you will find it hard work: the more milk, the more pressure, and the faster it comes out.

When you start learning, you will find muscles in your arms and hands that you did not know existed. They will ache with tiredness before you have even milked out a pint. That is why you should practise on a cow that can, if necessary, be finished off by someone else or by machine. If you get frustrated, the cow will sense it and will get upset herself; then you will never get the milk out. A cow with character can shut off the supply and not let a drop escape from her teats if she is annoyed, even if her udder is full to bursting. If you alarm her or lose your temper, she will react by urinating, which is not good for the milk in the bucket.

Use a three-legged stool: it is more manoeuvrable than a four-legged one and sometimes you will need to move quickly. Sit hard by the cow and at right angles to her; the closer you are the more control you have. It is customary to milk from the off (right) side, but consistency is what counts. Press your head firmly into her body so that you can feel any imminent movement. Do not let your hair tickle her: a cow has a sensitive hide; she feels every fly and every hair, and she reacts with a swish of her tail. Tails can be wet, muddy, or clogged with hardened mud and dung if grooming has been neglected, and a flick can be painful.

Grip the bucket between your knees so that you have complete control over it. You can then swing it rapidly out of range if necessary. For reasons of hygiene you should use a stainless-steel bucket, but that can be very noisy and cumbersome. There are heavy-duty plastic buckets which can withstand the boiling water needed to ensure scrupulous cleanliness. Cleanliness is essential: milk picks up bacteria very readily, and udders are also vulnerable to infection. Make sure that everything you use is scoured clean – the bucket and your hands for a start. Before you milk, while the cow is starting her feed, wash the udder well in warm water, using a clean cloth. Disposable cloths are best as they can be thrown away before they are unhygienic. Dairy farmers use a hot-water spray but an advantage of washing with a cloth is that it will stimulate the cow to let down her milk. Let-down does not mean that the milk comes pouring out of its own accord: it means that it drops in the bag and begins to fill the teats.

This stimulation is important. Some cows let down easily and require only your approach at the usual time of day, or the rattle of food going into the feed bucket (which is as good a reason as any for feeding the production ration at milking time). Most will be ready to let down by the time you have washed, but if not you

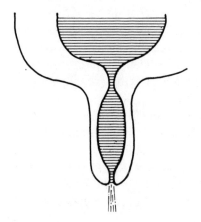

Fig 5 A full teat: milk from the udder cistern fills the teat when let-down is stimulated. To milk, close off the top of the teat by gripping with forefinger and thumb to trap the milk in the teat channel; empty the teat by squeezing progressively down it, applying pressure with the second finger, then the third, until the milk emerges. Release the grip to allow the teat to fill again.

should massage the udder until the milk drops. You will know when the cow is ready by beginning to milk: if nothing much is in the teat, keep massaging.

Watch a calf persuading let-down. It is pretty rough: it butts vigorously against the udder, bringing its head up and under and BAM! Then it has a frantic suck and if nothing is happening – BAM! – until it gets a result. I am not suggesting you use the udder as a punchbag: udders are both tough and vulnerable. But you understand the principle.

The milk is in four separate compartments in the udder, each with its own teat outlet, so you have to milk all four to get all the milk out. The teat works like a whisky dispenser once let-down has started: it fills with milk and then shuts off top and bottom so that a teatful is ready to be drawn out. The natural method of drawing it out is the calf's sucking. The calf channels its tongue along the teat to protect it from its front teeth, then it sucks and creates a lot of froth to help it.

A hand does not work quite like that! But take a hint from the calf – froth helps. It is much easier to milk a milk-moist teat than a dry one. As a beginner you might find that a little udder cream helps.

Have a look at the sketch of a full teat. To draw out the milk, you need to prevent it being forced back into the udder so you must apply a little pressure at the top of the teat. Never pinch above this point or you may damage the tissues. Maintain the pressure and squeeze moderately down the length of the teat, gradually encouraging the milk down until it spurts out. The first few squirts from each teat should be directed into a special 'strip cup' and checked for signs of trouble, for example, blood in the milk, or flaky clots (a sign of mastitis). The strippings should be discarded anyway: they might have been lying around since the last milking and might not be too fresh.

Practise a milking grip on a small brush. Clench your fingers around the handle. Tighten the grip between your thumb and first finger. Now tighten the second finger, then the third and finally the little finger. Practise that motion: it is alien to your hand, which naturally squeezes from the little finger towards the forefinger.

Now do the same to that fat, full teat. Milk two teats at a time,

Friesian: The mass-production cow: lots of milk, lots of beef. Originally from Holland; now familiar all over Britain

Welsh Black: Robust and hardy hill breed, a native of Wales since before the Romans. The North Wales strain is more compact than the rangy South Wales variety

one in each hand. It is probably easier to milk the two back teats together as they are sometimes smaller than the front ones, but it does not really matter how you pair them. Take the nearest in your left hand and the furthest in your right. Squeeze with alternate hands. At first you will get only a trickle and you will feel frustrated. It could well take twenty minutes to get a few pints, but do not worry. You will learn. Practise.

In due course the milk will come purling out in big satisfying jets and you will get that lovely froth in the bucket that says you are milking well. The cow will be standing with half-closed eyes looking blissful. With luck.

If you really cannot get the hang of the squeezing technique, try the 'stripping' motion – easier, but not to be recommended for any length of time as it is hard on the udder and on the hands, and it takes longer. Milk with the thumb and a couple of fingertips, gripping (but not too hard) the top of the teat and sliding the grip down until the milk comes out. Never squeeze too hard or stretch the teat excessively in your frustration. This method is used at the end of a milking session to strip the cow, that is, to get every last drop out of the udder. You do this for your own sake, to get *all* the cream because cream rises so that the last strippings are the creamiest, and for the cow's sake to prevent udder troubles. Also, if you leave milk in the udder the cow's body will assume it is not required and will in due course reabsorb it; next time you will get less milk, as nature believes that the 'calf' is weaning itself and there is therefore no point in producing too much milk. Regular failure to strip out can dry up the milk supply well in advance of the proper time.

It is generally believed that a cow only lets down her milk for eight minutes and that milking should be completed within that time. Once you have stimulated let-down, allow nothing to distract you from milking her out: you must finish the job. But do not panic about how long it is taking. If you have chosen a reasonable cow she will be lenient with you, though she might not think much of it. She will get bored, if nothing else, and once her natural good nature has run out, so has your milk supply. Give up, because you will not get another drop.

After milking you can occasionally give the teats a dip – you can buy special iodine teat dips which keep the teats supple and germ-free. Like everything else, dips are usually sold only in bulk, for herds of a hundred head, so you would do well to be on good terms with a farmer and beg small amounts off him. Put the liquid in a small jar (for example, a spice jar) not much bigger than the teat, diluting according to instructions, and dip the teat right in. This practice should help fend off mastitis, which is one of the most unpleasant udder problems. Mastitis is highly infectious and can be quite a problem in dairy herds, though it should be avoidable with a house cow. The warning signs are clots in the first strippings, an abnormal swelling and heat in a teat, and any hardness in the udder – not to be confused with normal udder tightness as the milk drops. Once you have felt a mastitic udder (ask a local farmer to show you an example) you will know what to watch for. An old remedy for hard udders is to massage well with plain soap and warm water for several days, stripping out three or four times a day. Nowadays it is wisest to consult a vet and get the trouble cleared up quickly. There is a danger that an infected quarter might never again function as a milk-producing organ. The veterinary treatment consists of injections in the rump and the insertion of antibiotics into the teat channel itself (intramammary infusion). You can do it yourself once you have watched how. You are not supposed to drink the milk for seventy-two hours after the last intramammary infusion, because although only one teat might be treated the antibiotic finds its way into the whole body and affects all the quarters. Never be tempted to curtail the treatment once you have started, even if you see an instant improvement. Any course of antibiotics *must* be carried right through.

Mastitis can be caused by damage to the teat from a rough calf, or by a cow treading on her own teat as she rises, or snagging herself on barbed-wire. Sometimes the injury penetrates to the milk duct and the cow leaks milk non-stop. Do not worry – the wound will scab over in due course – but keep it clear of infection.

A sudden drop in yield can be a sign of mastitis, or it can be attributed to less drastic circumstances, such as a change of routine, something unusual in the milking parlour, lack of fresh drinking water, or bulling. But take heed: a drop in yield is often the first sign of sickness of one kind or another.

If you have a cow with fidgety back feet, watch out! She will end up with a foot in the bucket and there will be due cause to swear. Some cows are merely restless and easy enough to anticipate. Some are ticklish and are aiming to kick flies off their bellies. (They can be trained out of this habit: Rosie had one uninhibited whack with the empty plastic bucket and she is quick to learn. If the flies are really teasy and I fail to brush them away for her, she scrapes up dust with a front foot and flicks it on to her belly, so the milk gets dusty.) A shudder or twitch along the body warns you that something is tickling somewhere. You get fewer flies if you milk indoors. You can spray a cow with special insecticide to discourage flies but you might find that the high-pitched hiss of the aerosol will send her at full speed across the field. I have found an aerosol is an invaluable herding aid: I merely take the cap off the spray and Rosie is over the horizon in no time.

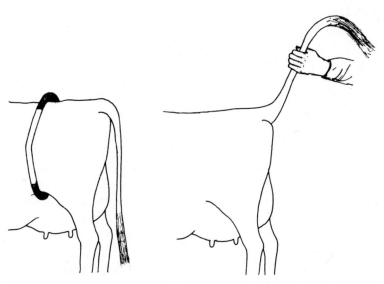

Fig 6 Anti-kicking techniques: (a) an anti-kick bar, one end of which hooks into the loose skin by the udder and the other over the cow's back (b) holding the cow's tail erect will prevent kicking and fidgeting.

If a cow is about to urinate, you will feel her gathering up her belly and then she will shift her back feet forward and apart, arching her back and lifting her tail. You cannot stop her: just get everything out of the way. Then wash the udder all over again before you carry on milking.

Some cows are inveterate kickers. The most powerful part of the action is backwards or sideways, so if you sit close as you milk you will not get hurt, though the bucket might go for six. If your cow really does kick, rather than brush away minor irritations or lift her foot absentmindedly, there are a few tricks you can try before you sell her and get a more amenable milker. You can milk with your right hand only (a bore): run your left arm in front of her right hind leg and grasp the back of her left hind leg with your hand so that your arm acts as an anti-kick barrier. (If she is trying to kick *you*, she has the sense to aim with the nearest leg only.) Alternatively, you can get someone else to grasp her tail about a third of its length from the root and hold it erect: this will stop all manner of fidgeting and is useful if the vet asks you to keep her quiet. You can hobble her feet together, or you can tie a rope very tightly round her waist. You can buy an anti-kick device, one end of which hooks over her back and the other into her groin. Poor cow. It is better to get a milder beast: milking should be a pleasure, not a battle.

Now, what to do with that hard-earned milk? You are not allowed to sell it unless you have registered with the Ministry and to do that you must meet some strict criteria designed to protect the consumer. You must milk in an approved building, with hot and cold water on tap, proper drainage, and a high degree of hygiene. You must remove the milk to a separate dairy for treatment, and reduce its temperature immediately. Your 'herd' must be free from tuberculosis and brucellosis. If you wish to pursue the legitimate selling of milk, contact the Ministry's District Veterinary Officer (DVO): he will send a couple of inspectors to tell you how to convert your premises to their standards. Then you can contact the Milk Marketing Board, who are currently bound to collect your milk and sell it for you (if you are approved) even if it is only one pint a day. For reasons of economy, however, the MMB is gradually phasing out churn collection in favour of bulk milk tanks, so you will find it better to get a licence to sell direct to the public from your 'farm', which means inspections of your methods of bottling and regular spot-checks by the MMB and the Ministry.

It cannot be emphasised enough how important hygiene is in dairying. Utensils should be rinsed free of milk using *cold* water (if your first rinse is hot, milk will go off in that utensil however clean you think it is) and then scalded with boiling water or steam. They should be dried outside in the fresh air. Try not to use cloths, which too readily harbour bacteria – use paper towels for drying if necessary.

It is as well to get yourself a supply of milk socks. These are filters designed for bulk milk tanks but they are fine for filtering the dust and small udder hairs out of home milk. They are sold by the hundred and should last you quite a while: use a fresh one every few days, rinsing very thoroughly (cold water first) each time they are used. You could use coffee filter papers but they tend to disintegrate.

Deal with the milk immediately after milking, because the cream begins to set quite quickly. If you can, refrigerate it straight away. If not, cool it by putting the bucket in a cold-water bath. Cooled quickly, milk should keep in the fridge for four or five days. If you do not have a fridge, store the milk in a running stream or a well or somewhere where it will remain at 40°F (4·4°C) or less. If you want it to keep longer, you can pasteurise it: heat in a double boiler to 150°F (65.6°C) and maintain the temperature for half an hour; cool quickly and refrigerate.

Milk can take many forms. The most obvious are cream, butter, cream cheese, cottage or curd cheese, hard cheese, and yoghurt. For many of these you need cream, so cream must be your first concern.

Cream

Good cow's milk readily sets its cream if left in a wide-necked container for twenty-four hours. Then you can just skim off the thick skin of cream from the top of the milk using a saucer and starting at one edge, trying to avoid collecting any milk at the same time. You can invest in a proper cream floater, which has holes in it to let the milk escape. You can siphon the milk out from under the cream. You can set the cream in a special trough with a plug in the bottom so that the milk can be drained out leaving the cream sticking to the trough, or you can create a container like a beer cask with a tap near the base. You can buy a mechanical separator, which extracts pure cream by centrifugal force, but this gadget is expensive, cumbersome, and a devil to clean. A saucer is simpler, if less efficient. If you leave the milk for another twelve hours after the first skimming, you will get some more cream.

Cream keeps in the fridge for a few days if you want to accumulate it. Put it in screw-top jars or in bowls made airtight with aluminium foil: if cream is exposed to the air it tends to get an unsightly crust on it, and like all milk products it readily picks up smells from other foods in the fridge. It is also possible to keep cream in the deep-freeze for use when the milk supply has run out.

The thickness and amount of cream you get from a gallon of milk varies according to the breed, the individual cow, the stage of her lactation, the time of year, the quality of her food, and the method of separation. You tend to get a maximum percentage of butter fat in the milk in winter or as the lactation curve drops away.

To clot cream (which makes it last longer), stand the milk for twenty-four hours in a cool place until the cream rises, then heat gently in the same container to 150–170°F (65.6–76.7°C). Cool for twelve hours, then skim off the cream.

Use sour cream for cooking beef Stroganoff and other exciting gourmet dishes, or try it as a basis for butter with a distinctive taste. But make your first butter with 'sweet' cream, storing the cream in the fridge until you have accumulated enough to render butter-making practical. It takes almost as much labour to make one pound of butter as it does to make six. Aim to have a butter-making session perhaps twice a week.

Fig 7 Dairy equipment: (a) Blow churn for butter-making (b) plunger churn
(c) Scotch hands – corrugated wooden bats for working and shaping butter.

Butter (made from cream)
There are six basic steps in butter-making. First ripen the cream,
then churn it; next, wash the butter granules, then squeeze them
dry; then salt and work the butter, and finally wrap and store it.
The churning takes less time if the cow is early on in her lactation,
or is on lush pasture, or if the cream is 'ripe'.

1 *Ripen the cream.* Cream should be brought to a temperature
of 52–60°F (11·1–15·6°C) in hot weather or 58–66°F
(14·4–18·9°C) in cooler weather before it is ready to churn. Too
warm or too cold, you might never get to the butter stage or you
might go clean through it. Use cream which is at least twenty-four
hours old: take it out of the fridge and stand it at room
temperature overnight, and in winter it won't hurt to stand it near
the stove.

2 *Churn the cream.* Your aim is to agitate the cream until the hidden butterfat particles are persuaded together into little granules of yellow butter, separating themselves from the buttermilk. There are various types of churn: I use a Blow churn, which is a large glass jar with wooden paddles turned by a handle in the lid. For small amounts of cream you can shake it in a jam jar until your arms ache; you can roll a tightly lidded jar on the kitchen table or attach it to the rocking chair; you can paddle with (very clean) fingers for hours; or you can take a tip from the Argentinian cowboys and tie jars of cream to the saddle and ride about for a few hours to shake the cream into butter! You can use an eggbeater (laborious and messy) or better still an electric mixer with variable speeds, starting on a low one. You can find old-fashioned (that is, 'antique', expensive and rare) wooden churns of varying ingenuity, powered by muscle or by dogs on paddle-wheels or children on see-saws. Electric power takes the arm-ache out of butter-making but it is not necessarily any quicker. Whatever the method, make sure that the implement is easily cleanable and that it is always scrupulously clean before use. Cold-water rinse, scald, air dry, every time. Wooden paddles 'cobble' if you fail to use the cold rinse first.

Start churning. At first the cream is splashy, so stand well back or contain it. Next it will thicken, and this stage might take up to ten minutes. Keep churning the thick cream until – take care – it suddenly goes thin and splashy again. It is about to 'come'. It is getting a golden tinge and forming little pellets of butter, sloshing around in the thin buttermilk. It can take anything up to forty-five minutes to reach this point. Go slow now: do not churn too much more, because if the butter lumps get bigger than wheat grains you will have difficulty in washing the butter properly.

3 *Wash.* Get a big bowl and put a clean nylon sieve across it. Empty the milk and butter mixture into the sieve and let the buttermilk drain into the bowl. (Buttermilk is rich in milk-sugar and proteins and can be drunk fresh or allowed to thicken in a warm place and labelled 'cultured'.) Put the butter granules back into the churn and cover with water at churning temperature. If the water is too cold the granules will shrink and pass through the

sieve; if it is too warm they will get big and soft and you will never be able to rinse them thoroughly. Churn again for a few seconds; sieve and drain. Repeat this sequence several times until the draining water comes through absolutely clear without a trace of milk in it. If you do not wash thoroughly the butter will turn rancid in no time.

4 *Squeeze dry*. Now you want to remove as much moisture as possible from the butter. Take a clean board and dump enough of the butter granules on it to form a thin layer. Tilt the board so that the water can drain away. Use a strong palette knife or proper corrugated wooden butterhands to press the butter on the board and squeeze out the water. Do not smear the butter at this stage. Get out every possible drop of moisture: the less the water content, the longer the butter will keep.

5 *Salt and work*. Next, work the butter, adding salt to taste. The more salt, the longer the butter keeps, but not many people like excessively salted butter. Test by tasting: if it is too salty, wash it. Work the butter until it is smooth, without air gaps, then shape it as you please – and perhaps stamp it with a personal motif.

6 *Wrap and store*. You must wrap butter or it will not keep well and it will pick up taints. Use greaseproof paper, then tinfoil. Keep it reasonably airtight. For storing large quantities of butter, you can either salt it more than usual and pack it firmly in a large earthenware container with an airtight cover, or you can put it in a deep-freeze.

Cream Cheese (made from cream)
I make cream cheese by default. If the cream I am saving for butter-making goes a little too ripe, and any residual milk underneath it goes solid, I leave it to drip through muslin draped over a sieve over a bowl. Tie the cloth at the top. After a couple of days all the smelly whey has dripped through into the bowl and I am left with sweet cream cheese. It can be used as it is, or flavoured with chives, pineapple chunks, walnuts, herbs, etc. It can also be used to make cheesecake.

Other people make cream cheese by heating cream slowly in a double boiler almost to boiling point, adding a little rennet or lemon juice to curdle it, then breaking up the curds and straining, and finally pressing between two plates.

Rennet can be bought from good grocers or by mail order (see Appendix, p 101) or you can make your own if you find yourself with a dead calf: take out the stomach, clean it and pickle it in salt water. One small slice is all you need as a 'starter' for cheese-making. Rennet is a substance in the lining of the abomasum (the largest and only developed stomach in the newborn animal) which naturally curdles the milk to make it more digestible to the calf. Rennet is not usually needed to make cream cheese from double cream but it does help if you are using single cream.

Cottage or Curd Cheese (made from whole, skim or butter milk)
Let the milk curdle (or encourage it with acids or rennet); chop up the thick curds and strain as for cream cheese.

Hard Cheeses (made from whole milk)
To make 'proper' cheese you need space, equipment, time, skill, and more milk than you get from one cow. Cheese-making becomes a true art, and every 'dairy' produces an individual cheese. It all depends on what bacteria happen to be present: you might end up with anything from a Cheddar-type to a Brie, or something quite inedible. Variety comes from how much cream you have in the milk, how long you leave the cheese to ripen, how much pressure you apply, what moulds you care to inject into it, what the local climate and vegetation are like, what time of year it is – the factors are endless.

Basically, all cheese is made from milk curd which has been separated from the whey (usually by the agency of rennet) and ripened. Here are the basic stages:

1 Ripen the milk overnight at about 50–60°F (10–15·6°C), then heat the milk to 85–105°F (29·4–40·6°C), depending on the cheese.
2 Add rennet diluted in water, and mix thoroughly.

3 Stand in a warm place until the curd forms firmly (about half an hour at 85–90°F (29·4–32·2°C) – the surface of the curd should break cleanly if you insert your finger at an angle under the skin and lift).

4 Break the curd into even-sized pieces, say $\frac{1}{2}$in across. To do this, cut with a long-bladed knife inserted vertically: make a criss-cross pattern; then put the knife in at a good angle and cut in along the same lines.

5 Heat the curds very slowly to about 100°F (37·8°C), paddling gently with your fingers to keep the pieces separate and to spread the heat throughout, until the curds are firm enough not to stick to each other.

6 Drain off the whey by straining the curds through muslin or cheesecloth.

7 Salt the curds and work them: if you want a very firm cheese, squeeze the curds into a firm ball; for crumbly cheese keep them looser.

8 Shape into a cake not more than 6in across, with no cracks in it, and hold it together with bands of moistened cheesecloth.

9 Press the cheese between flat surfaces with a heavy weight (for example, bricks) on top: to keep the shape make a wooden mould. Turn after twelve hours and press from the other end.

10 Remove the swaddling and place the cheese in a cool frost-free place to ripen. Turn daily until the rind is formed, treat the rind with salt and butter or paraffin wax, and then turn on alternate days until ripe – say three to four weeks. Eat when mature, say, two months. Good luck.

Yoghurt (made from skim or whole milk or thin cream)
Warm the milk to 95–110°F (35–43·4°C). Add a 'starter' (a spoonful of plain shop yoghurt or a commercial yoghurt starter) and maintain the temperature for several hours by putting the container in a haybox or by using a thermos flask or leaving it on the Aga. The longer you keep it warm, the stronger and firmer the yoghurt.

Desserts

Junket is milk curdled with rennet and eaten immediately. You can buy junket tablets at the grocers in various flavours, or you can add nutmeg or rum. For Devonshire junket cover the set junket with a layer of brandy-flavoured whipped cream and sprinkle with nutmeg or with cinnamon and sugar.

Syllabub is made with milk fresh from the cow, poured from a height over wine, cider, ale or brandy, to make a frothy mixture which is sweetened and flavoured with spices. You can use double cream instead: whisk a couple of egg whites stiffly, fold in 4oz caster sugar, the juice of half a lemon, $\frac{1}{4}$pt sweet white wine and $\frac{1}{2}$pt whipped cream. Chill and decorate with lemon slices. You can add a couple of spoonfuls each of brandy and sherry instead of white wine if you prefer.

Ice-cream is best made from double cream. There are two methods of making ice-cream: (1) heat $\frac{1}{4}$pt milk with $1\frac{1}{2}$oz sugar and pour on to a beaten egg, stir, return to the saucepan and cook gently until it thickens, strain, add vanilla essence, cool, fold in $\frac{1}{4}$pt half-whipped cream, pour into freezing tray and put in the ice box – you will have to stir it every twenty minutes until it is half frozen, or add a teaspoonful of gelatine to the pint to improve texture; (2) whip $\frac{1}{2}$pt double cream, stir in $\frac{1}{2}$pt fruit juice gradually, add enough sugar to make it taste very sweet, half-freeze, stir, and freeze.

Beestings

For the first four days after calving, cow's milk is hardly recognisable as such. It is a thick yellow substance (colostrum) which will save the newborn calf's life by giving it an instant dose of protection against germs as well as readily digestible protein. Colostrum milk is also called beestings, and it is considered a delicacy as a drink just as it is – but it is a matter of taste! It turns into egg custard without any help from eggs: warm in a saucepan, add sugar or honey, turn into a greased ovenproof dish, sprinkle with nutmeg or cinnamon, and bake until set, about forty-five minutes at 325°F (163°C).

6 Health

A house cow will probably remain healthier than the commercial dairy animal. She is not subject to the same stresses: she is not expected to produce huge yields; she does not have to fight for her share of the food; she has personal attention. Mind you, she is in an unnatural situation: cows are, after all, herd animals. But there are compensations.

The lack of a herd means that contagious diseases, such as mastitis, are avoidable. On the other hand, if you have just one cow rather than a hundred, she is all-important to you and you will want to be aware of possible health problems and how to deal with them. Vets are invaluable, but expensive, and there are things that you can do yourself once you know what and how. But do make sure you have a good and sympathetic vet.

A healthy cow has a moist nose free from mucus, a bright eye, a soft and pliable hide with a bloom on it, a good appetite, and a general appearance of alertness. An off-colour cow tends to stand with her head down and show a general lassitude. She will be slow to come in for milking and not particularly interested in food. Feel her skin: if the hide is tight and dull, the cow may be feverish or have some digestive problem. A sick cow's eyes may be sunken, or staring and dull. Scouring (diarrhoea) is a sure sign of trouble. Except when she is bulling or calving, there should be no discharge from the vulva. A healthy cow's breath smells fresh and sweet; her urine should not smell too strong and certainly should not be too dark or have blood in it. If the milk yield drops suddenly, or the milk smells of peardrops, check her over.

The normal temperature is 101–102°F (38·3–38·9°C). If she seems miserable, check her temperature by putting a greased thermometer up her rectum. The normal pulse rate is about sixty to the minute – check the artery at the base of the tail.

Other symptoms to watch out for are unsteady gait, hard droppings, clots in the milk, hot and painful udder, abnormal discharge from the vulva, lameness, profuse salivation, laboured breathing, loss of cud, inability to rise, swollen joints, persistent coughing – one could go on, but it is likely that with only one cow you will notice that she is off-colour before specific symptoms become apparent.

If your cow looks sick, house her immediately in a well-strawed, clean loose-box. If she has a temperature, keep her warm. Give her a laxative diet, for example, bran mash with molasses or linseed cake added to encourage her appetite. Treat her quietly and avoid stress. If you know you cannot cope, get the vet. But do not worry: you might never see a sign of illness in your cow until she dies peacefully of old age. As long as your routines are clean and regular, you will have little trouble.

Some of the more common problems are described below. (Methods of injecting and drenching are described in detail later.) An asterisk indicates that it would be advisable to call the vet for treatment of the problem; a double asterisk means that the vet should be called immediately.

Acetonaemia

Loss of appetite; peardrop smell on breath or in milk; constipation. Associated with high protein/starch ratio in diet or inferior quality silage. Try to maintain appetite, and exercise without undue stress. Give glycerine or molasses to stimulate appetite, or 1oz potassium chlorate in water for three days. Veterinary treatment might include injections to stimulate metabolism.

**Bloat

Cow swells up like a balloon: comes from overeating, particularly on new spring grass or white clover. Cow cannot belch and gases accumulate in rumen; death can follow. Prevent by restricting spring grazing until she is used to it, or feed roughage before turning out in the morning. Treatment must be immediate. A drench should help while you are waiting for the vet – silicone drenches are best, though linseed oil may reduce the surface tension of the rumen liquids. Veterinary treatment will probably be a trochar and canulla – literally punching a hole in the side of the stomach to let the methane escape.

**Brucellosis (contagious abortion)
Premature calving. Can cause undulant fever in humans. The Ministry must be notified. The cow will have to be destroyed if brucellosis is diagnosed; there is no remedy. If she calves prematurely, isolate her from any other cattle. Prevention is by vaccination of heifers between the ages of 90 and 180 days. Always buy from accredited stock, or get a blood test before bringing in new stock.

Constipation
Hard droppings, straining. Drench with linseed, etc to get things moving. Alter diet and give bran or molasses. Constipation and loss of appetite may indicate fever or chill. If defecation ceases altogether, get veterinary advice. See also *Poisoning*, below.

*Digestive Problems
A tight skin with no bloom; usually a decrease in appetite and milk production. Constant grinding of the teeth indicates pain and the possibility of a foreign body in the stomach, often pieces of wire or old nails left carelessly lying about. Young animals tend to swallow things like string and plastic and may die. Drenching might help in mild cases; otherwise seek advice.

**Foot-and-mouth Disease
Lameness accompanied by profuse salivation, caused by blisters on feet and tongue. If confirmed, the police and the Ministry must be informed immediately, and the animal will have to be slaughtered.

*Gynaecological Problems
In all problems with the reproductive system, consult the vet. Failure to come bulling after calving may be attributable to any one of a number of causes. Persistent bulling usually indicates cystic ovaries. A foetid or white discharge from the vulva in a pregnant animal indicates a dead calf or pyometritis (pus in the womb). Such a discharge after calving may indicate retained afterbirth (normally the afterbirth is shed naturally within twenty-four hours of calving); the vet can remove it manually after three

or four days. A purulent discharge after calving is caused by endometritis (inflammation of the womb) and is a common sequel to a difficult calving, the birth of twins, or retained afterbirth.

*Husk
Persistent coughing, loss of condition, skin tight and dull, droppings loose and smelly. Caused by lungworms. Dose young stock *before* there is any trouble, in early July and before housing for the winter, by subcutaneous injection or with oral dosage. Calves can be given oral vaccine by the vet to prevent infestation: give six weeks and four weeks before turning out to grass. Do not graze calves on pasture which has been used by older cattle during the previous twelve months. If husk does develop, house the animal immediately in a clean loose-box, feed generously, and consult the vet about dosing.

**Hypomagnesaemia (tetany, grass staggers)
Normally occurs with spring or autumn flush of grass. Fall in level of blood magnesium: animal becomes unduly nervous, ears twitch, eyes roll, rapid collapse. Avoid stress and handle very gently; call vet immediately. Prevention should be standard practice in spring and autumn: feed 2oz calcined magnesium per day, or get a magnesium-boosted cake from the mill. Gradual introduction to pasture and continuation of some hay feeding initially at spring turnout helps prevention.

Itching
Could be lice – insecticides are available. Put an impregnated back rub in the field. Mange – which is more than the usual seasonal moult – causes loss of hair on neck, rump and withers. See also *Ringworm* and *Warbles*, below.

Lameness
Make sure the lameness is not due to foot-and-mouth disease. Check for stones between the claws. Check for foot-rot caused by standing in dung for long periods. A strained shoulder might cause limping. Treat a hot foot by wrapping in a bag of hot bran. A foot bath used regularly will help avoid foot problems: 5 per cent formalin or copper sulphate solution. Keep hooves trimmed.

Fencing: strut support for a straining post. The struts counter the strain of the barbed-wire and are shaped to fit notches cut into the post

Field corral. A small railed area is useful as a holding pen for veterinary inspection and artificial insemination. Paved with heavy slabs or concrete, it also acts as an open-air milking stall

Calf shed. The shed is built so that the cow can reach over the front palisade to wash the calf without the calf being able to reach the udder. Shutters at each end can be removed for extra ventilation, and the extended roof gives shelter for the cow. Because the shed becomes a familiar

Mastitis
Bacterial infection of the udder. Abnormally high temperature, clots or pus in foremilk strippings, hardening and inflammation of udder, yield drop, loss of appetite. Milk the infected teat last to avoid spreading infection. Massage udder with soap to make it more supple and strip out three or four times a day. Seek veterinary advice regarding antibiotic treatment (usually intramammary infusions); you *must* complete the course and should not consume the milk for seventy-two hours after final treatment. Prevention by strict hygiene and regular teat dipping in iodine solution; cows may be treated with a long-acting antiobiotic as a preventative during the dry period. Contagious.

Milk Fever (hypocalcaemia)
Can occur shortly after calving: by yielding milk the cow is losing too much calcium too quickly. Nervousness, paddling of the feet, staring eyes, unsteady gait, unable to rise once she is down (though inability to rise can also be caused by injury to the spine). Instant action essential. Treat quietly. To prevent: only partially milk a newly-calved cow for the first few days; check the mineral content of rations, particularly calcium, phosphorus and vitamin D. Sometimes a massive dose of vitamin D is given prior to calving as a preventive measure but is not completely reliable.

New Forest Eye (contagious keratoconjunctivitis)
Thought to be a fly-borne disease, which is aggravated by dust. Jerseys are particularly prone. The eye develops a watery discharge and eventually a 'blind' film may form if untreated. In fact some animals may go blind in the affected eye, though often they recover without treatment. Antibiotics are the cure: these can be in the form of ointments or injection into the eye.

Pneumonia
Abnormal temperature, laboured breathing, animal probably looking back along its body, possibly cough and nasal discharge. House immediately: an old blanket is useful to keep the animal warm.

Ringworm

Barė patches with skin thickening into a characteristic scab, particularly on face. Infectious, and humans can also be affected. Caused by a fungus. Very unsightly, though some animals do not seem worried by it and it usually goes away after three or four months. More common in younger animals. Isolate and treat animal with specific ringworm dressings, or give oral fungicide. Thoroughly clean out affected housing and treat with anti-fungal application; clean other equipment with 5 per cent formalin solution.

Swollen Joints

These might be caused by septicaemia (blood poisoning) or merely be damage from a hard bed. Around calving time swollen hocks in heifers mean that they have not had enough exercise.

Teat Troubles

A 'pea' in the teat is a hard lump in the teat channel; sometimes you can squeeze it out yourself, otherwise the vet can do a small operation. Warts on teats might cause kicking during milking and need to be removed by the vet. Sore teats can be treated with medicated vaseline or udder cream. Injured teats should be cleaned thoroughly, and dusted with sulphanilamide powder or dressed with iodine (teat dip); if badly cut they will need stitching. There are a number of virus diseases which cause lesions of the teats. Watch out, too, for mastitis.

*Tuberculosis

Largely under control but outbreaks still occur. Cattle undergo regular compulsory checking by the Ministry. Loose and stinking dung is a symptom. Notify the Ministry if confirmed.

Warbles

Warble flies affect a third of cattle, especially in hot dry seasons. The grubs migrate through the body until they form lumps on the back and loins between March and June. The lumps eventually burst and leave permanent holes in the hide. Prevention is important: dress annually with special systemic warble dressings applied only at the time of year recommended by the manufacturer. Wrong timing can kill the migrating larvae in the spinal canal and cause paralysis or death of the cow. The dressing is diluted as prescribed and the thick, oily liquid is dribbled along the spine from shoulder to tail so that it trickles gradually down the animal's sides. Follow instructions carefully, and only treat a milking cow immediately after milking and not less than six hours before the next milking. Do not treat sick animals.

**Poisoning

Summon the vet immediately you suspect an animal has eaten something poisonous or shows symptoms. A list of poisonous plants can be found in the Appendix (p 111), and an additional and potent source of poison is lead paint, which calves in particular develop a liking for. Make sure there is no paintwork within reach.

The symptoms of poisoning are generally great distress and loss of appetite. Other symptoms include salivation; vomiting (rare in cattle, and very forceful – usually caused by eating rhododendrons); colic, which causes a cow to grunt as she exhales and which may eventually be accompanied by convulsions and even death. A belly pain is indicated by grinding of the teeth and by attempts to kick the stomach.

Sudden death can be caused by the cow eating yew or plants containing cyanogenetic glycosides, for example, a quantity of fruit kernels, apple and pear pips, laurel, linseed, millet, sorghums, wild white clover, some rushes – all of which yield prussic acid. In such cases, to save the animal you must immediately give sugar, or a 5 per cent solution of hyposulphite of soda, or ammonia or ammonium carbonate well diluted with water. Give orally if possible, or make the animal inhale ammoniacal fumes. The symptoms of prussic acid poisoning are rapid breathing for a few seconds followed by the animal falling on its side. Spasms can be followed quickly by death. A cow's rumen can neutralise reasonable quantities of prussic acid but the animal may develop goitres or thyroid problems.

You cannot pump out a poisoned cow's stomach: you can only get the vet to perform a rumenotomy, that is, cut into the rumen through the flank, though this is seldom a practical proposition. Once emptied, the rumen must be filled again as quickly as possible or the animal may die; have ready some hay chaff, mixed with bran and crushed oats, scalded with boiling water and kept at body temperature – three large bucketfuls at least. Have eggs, milk, sugar or yeast to hand in case the vet needs them.

To soothe the membranes of the mouth and stomach in the case of irritant poisons, prepare a demulcent of 1 doz eggs, 1lb sugar and $\frac{1}{2}$gal milk (halve the quantity for a yearling). This will soothe but not cure.

Diarrhoea is a sign that nature is doing its best to shoot the poison out of the system and in the early stages you should let nature take its course. But persistent diarrhoea leads to dehydration and the animal will need astringents: kaolin powder or chlorodyne are best, or boiled milk fed cool, cold gruels of flour and starch, eggs – and even a tot of whisky might help.

Constipation, on the other hand, may be caused by local paralysis. Useful laxatives are medicinal liquid paraffin for preference, given as a drench, or linseed (which may cause nausea), or castor oil. A laxative diet might include molasses or golden syrup, warm fresh milk, hay tea, yeast, or oatmeal gruel.

Unless the vet specifically recommends them, do not use the more drastic purgatives such as Epsom salts or aloes in treating poisoning.

Fits may occur in the later stages of poisoning and may be followed by deep coma or death. All you can do is keep the animal quiet and make sure that it does not injure itself during the fit.

Common sequels to poisoning are loss of cud, anaemia and debility. If acids have been used to counteract poisoning, give 1lb baker's yeast in lukewarm water to restore the balance of bacteria in the rumen, or in the case of alkaline medication give 1lb sugar dissolved in 1pt vinegar. For anaemia, give a high-protein diet with added minerals, particularly common salt and iron. To make the best use of iron, copper and cobalt need to be present as traces in the mixture. A likely after-effect of poisoning is that the recovered animal develops a craving for the very plant which poisoned it, so make quite sure that such plants are well out of reach. The craving can be so acute that all other foods are refused and the animal makes strenuous efforts to reach the poisonous plant. The best answer is to ensure that the animal has no access to poisonous plants in the first place.

Don't be alarmed by this catalogue of ailments: you will be either careless or unlucky to experience any of them. Most house cows have long and pleasantly uncomplicated lives and give little cause for concern. Keep a close eye on your cow, get to know her so that you can spot potential problems before they become actual problems, be strict with hygiene, manage grazing sensibly, introduce dietary changes gradually, take sound preventive measures, liaise with your vet, and treat your cow with due consideration. With these precautions you should not go far wrong.

Notifiable Diseases
You are legally bound to notify the police of the following diseases immediately they are suspected: anthrax, cattle plague, foot-and-mouth disease, pleuro-pneumonia, and tuberculosis.

In addition, the Ministry must be informed, and they will also have to be told of a case of brucellosis. It is advisable to be on good terms with your local DVO anyway. He will be an early contact as he must, under the Brucellosis Eradication Scheme, give his permission before you can have cattle on your land.

If an animal contracts any of these notifiable diseases, it will in most cases have to be slaughtered, and the Ministry will partially compensate you for its loss. You and your animals will also be subject to certain restrictions designed to lessen the risk of the disease spreading to uninfected herds. These are listed in the Ministry's free booklet *At the Farmer's Service*, which also gives details of compensation, grants and subsidies, advisory services, regional addresses, etc.

Dead Animals
The Ministry will advise you on the disposal of the carcass of an animal slaughtered compulsorily. Your local hunt kennels will welcome most other carcasses, whether calf or full-grown cow, and will remove them for you. They will also take unwanted live

animals. A live animal too old to keep can be worth money if you can bear to send her to market for the meat companies, who pay according to bodyweight and condition. It is a rotten way for an old friend to go, but at least her meat and hide will be put to good use. A sick animal should not be sent to market: occasionally an animal may be sold as a casualty direct for slaughter, in which case it may need a veterinary certificate. Generally, if an animal is sick or very poor she goes to a knacker's yard or is put down on the farm. You are not allowed to slaughter an animal yourself. If you have raised a calf for beef you must get it killed by a licensed slaughterer, who will butcher it for you.

How to Drench

A drench is the means by which liquids are given to a cow which is unwilling or unable to feed. Use a long-necked bottle (a beer bottle is fine if you clean it out thoroughly first). Hook your fingers into the side of the cow's mouth, palm against her muzzle, and raise her head so that her muzzle and neck are in a straight line a few degrees above parallel to the ground. Insert the neck of the bottle into the corner of her mouth, where there are no teeth. Trickle the liquid carefully and very gradually down her throat, giving her a chance to swallow it. Take care not to choke her.

How to Give Injections

Ask a vet to give you a practical demonstration of the injection techniques before you try any of them yourself. Always make sure the needle and the skin in the area to be injected are clean.

A subcutaneous injection is usually given just behind the shoulder: lift the skin and slide the needle under the outer hide, but not so far in that it penetrates the meat.

For an intramuscular injection, choose a fleshy part of the thigh or flank, avoiding bone. Slap the area once or twice with the heel of your hand to deaden it, then use your palm to drive the needle firmly straight through the skin into the muscle. Connect the syringe and withdraw the plunger slightly: if there is any blood in the tube you have hit a blood vessel and must try again.

For an intravenous injection you need more skill. Apply a tourniquet around the neck above the shoulder in order to plump up the jugular vein. Insert the needle and check that it *is* in the bloodstream. Release the tourniquet before injecting the drug.

An intramammary infusion requires no needle. Remove a little milk and swab the end of the teat with surgical spirit or methylated spirit. Push the nozzle up the opening of the teat channel and squeeze the tube to infuse the treatment.

Grooming

Cows enjoy being groomed and you will find that grooming removes plenty of dust and loose hair. It is important to groom the cow regularly, particularly if she is housed indoors in winter when she can get pretty itchy. If the cow is housed in winter it is also advisable to clip the thicker hairs along the spine and neck because that is where the lice will lodge. Keep her tail clean, combed and trimmed all year round: leave enough of a tassel to reach the flies, but there is no point in having it trailing in the mud. The udder hairs can also be trimmed. Keep an eye on her feet: the occasional walk on concrete helps to keep the hooves trimmed, otherwise they will need rasping or paring with blacksmith's pincers.

Insurance

Most insurance companies will cover your stock, though it is proportionately far more expensive to cover one or two animals than a hundred. You will want to insure against mortality, and there are special insurance categories for brucellosis, foot-and-mouth disease, anthrax, electrocution, tuberculosis, theft and straying, veterinary fees, etc. Shop around for the best rates and the most relevant policies.

7 Calving

In order to produce milk, a cow must first produce a calf. Once she has calved, her yield climbs to its peak at anything from three to six weeks after calving, and thereafter gradually declines at an expected rate of $2\frac{1}{2}$ per cent a week ($1\frac{1}{2}$ per cent for a first-calf heifer). An average lactation lasts, or is permitted to last, for 305 days.

Within three weeks of calving, the cow will come bulling, that is, on heat. She will come on again every three weeks for two days: most cows are accurate to the day, though the bulling interval varies from cow to cow, between eighteen and twenty-four days. It is usual to calve a cow at twelve-month intervals but this is up to you. Her gestation period is about forty weeks, so do something about getting her into calf about ten weeks after calving if you want a regular annual calf. She will continue bulling until you have got her into calf.

It is important to learn to recognise a bulling cow. Some animals are very obvious, particularly within the herd, and some people believe it must be difficult to spot bulling in the case of a lone animal. It depends on the cow. Signs of bulling include: restlessness and continual bawling into the distance; mounting other animals; allowing other cows to mount her (cows who are not bulling will mount a bulling cow but will not stand to be mounted themselves); a slight clear discharge from the vulva, followed twenty-four to forty-eight hours after she has finished bulling by a slight bloody discharge (the 'bulling string') which tends to stick to the tail; resting her chin on another animal; rubbing, sniffing and licking other animals. Her yield might drop, too, because she is reducing her grazing time by bawling and mounting.

If you have a 'silent heat' cow and cannot tell when she is bulling, your vet can give her a special injection to bring her on heat within a specific number of hours.

There are two ways to stock a cow. The simplest, if you have access, is to let a bull do it for you. He will know when she is ready for him. If you cannot get to a bull, call the 'AI' man. Both the Ministry and the Milk Marketing Board run an artificial insemination service. With AI you can use the 'bull of the day' of whatever breed you want (with a Jersey cow, for example, you can use a Jersey bull for pure-bred offspring, or an Angus or Hereford to put a bit of beef on the calf) or you can ask for a particular bull for an extra fee. You must telephone before 10am on the day you want your cow stocked and the inseminator will come during that day.

Look at the ovulation chart (Fig 8): time of service in relation to the heat period is important, and conception is more likely during the middle or towards the end of the heat period.

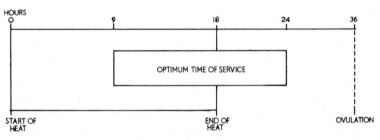

Fig 8 Ovulation chart

Have the cow tied up ready for the AI man. He will don long polythene gloves, take a frozen straw of semen from his ice container and plunge it into her vagina. If she is a quiet animal he will not need any help and the job will take ten seconds. Otherwise, be prepared to hold her tail erect to keep her still. After he has had a scrub-down he will write out your AI certificate, for which he will need to know the cow's name and ear number, and he will want some cash.

If the first insemination does not take, you normally get a second free, but further repeats are charged for because either you have misread the cow or you should have had the vet along to check her over. Failure to conceive may be caused by a number of factors, all needing veterinary diagnosis and treatment.

Heifers can come bulling as young as six months and it is not unknown for a heifer to try to mount a familiar human being. If she is big enough she will knock you flat on the ground: never turn your back on a bulling heifer. Do not be tempted to stock her too young – ideally she should have her first calf at the age of two or two-and-a-half years, but it depends on how well grown she is. Suckled heifers tend to develop earlier than bucket-reared animals. Poor feeding during the first six months of a heifer's life may lead to a weak and narrow pelvis which may cause problems in calving, and inadequate feeding during the first six months of her pregnancy, aggravated by overfeeding during the last six weeks, will mean she has not really got the reserves to cope with a fast-developing foetus. But overfeeding at any stage can create too much fat in the pelvic cavity, which can cause calving problems. Do not expect a first-calf heifer to produce an outsize calf: mate her with a bull of her own breed or with an Aberdeen Angus.

If you wish, your vet can confirm whether or not your cow is pregnant by rectal examination at eight to ten weeks after insemination. Once she is in calf, she will become more placid and content. You have nothing further to worry about in terms of her pregnancy until about eight or nine weeks before she is due to calve. At that stage you should begin to dry off her milk: the udder must be given a rest between calvings, to allow the tissues to rejuvenate themselves and to allow the cow to gather strength for her calving. Six to eight weeks is a good dry period; any shorter and the next lactation's yields tend to be depressed.

To dry her off, cut out the production ration, making sure she still has enough for maintenance. If she is having concentrates, cut them out completely and supplement with increased roughage in winter. Then milk her only once a day for a few days, or longer if she is still giving plenty; then reduce milking to every other day for a few days. Nature tends to withdraw the milk supply if it does not seem to be wanted and you will find that, after a week or two of reducing the occasions on which you milk, the yield will reduce noticeably. If she has been in milk for ten months or so she will probably be quite low already; indeed, some animals dry themselves off without any assistance and sometimes, to their owners' annoyance, several months before calving.

If she is still giving a lot of milk three months before calving, bear in mind that you will want to dry her off and start reducing her production ration then. Do not be too greedy for milk. If she is still giving more than a couple of gallons after the drying-off process is well under way, complete cessation of milking should develop udder pressure sufficient to cause reabsorption of the milk into the blood system over a period of two or three days. You must refrain from milking to relieve the pressure or in any way stimulating the udder.

Once you have decided on the last milking session, milk her out very thoroughly and leave her teats clean and preferably dipped in an iodine solution. Commercial farmers often give their dry cows a plug of long-acting penicillin up each teat to seal it off from any infection, but this should not be necessary for a house cow.

She may still bag up after the last milking but do not worry: the milk will be reabsorbed if you leave the udder alone.

About five or six weeks before the calving date you can, if the drying off is complete, start 'steaming up'. This is a process used to excess by commercial farmers to ensure maximum yields from their herds, and such pressure makes the cow's life shorter (on average a cow is kept in the milking herd for four lactations) and renders her udder susceptible to all sorts of troubles. Yet some steaming up is a good thing. The aim is to feed the cow an increasing amount of production ration before calving (making it slightly laxative) so that she is in good firm condition when she does calve and begins to yield. She needs some body reserves to fall back on for the first two months after calving.

Use concentrates rather than succulents or roughage for steaming up. A sensible ration for a house cow might be:

6–3 weeks before calving: build up from 2 to 4lb a day
3–0 weeks before calving: build up from 4 to 8lb a day

Heifers are steamed up more gently, if at all. Give a maximum of 6lb a day to a heifer.

Your aim is to have the cow fit not fat at calving. You may find that her appetite falls off as the calving date gets closer; cut down on her bulk feeds so that she will eat up her concentrates. In autumn restrict grazing and substitute 4–6lb hay to avoid scouring.

Now your cow is nearly ready to calve. You can either let her calve out of doors on grass, preferably in a clean field where no cattle have been for a year or two, or you can calve her indoors in a spacious, well-littered, draughtproof, disinfected loose-box. Wherever you want her to calve, it is only fair to give her a few days to get used to the environment so that she does not feel she is in alien surroundings.

The advantage of out-of-door calving is that it is much healthier: there is less risk of infection to cow and calf. The disadvantages become clear if there are any calving problems and you and the vet are peering around in the dark and the rain trying to help. The cow is better off indoors anyway if it is very wet, though dry cold is no hardship. If it is cold, however, the calf will be better off indoors as soon as possible.

A cow nearing calving might give several indications – or she might not. She should bag up a few days (and sometimes weeks) beforehand, and her udder may become so full it is uncomfortable. This is normally caused by too much steaming up too early or too suddenly. If the udder does look painfully congested you can massage it twice a day with an oily mixture, and as a last resort you can milk her to relieve the pressure. If the udder is very distended and if when you press your fingertips against the underside above the teats your fingers leave no depression, then you should pre-milk.

Make sure she does not get constipated at this stage, particularly if she is indoors. It is important for a cow to get plenty of exercise in the last two months before calving, so if she is indoors give her a regular daily outing. If she does get constipated, cut out a feed of concentrates and give her a bran mash with some molasses (4–5lb scalded bran + 1pt molasses).

During the last two or three days before she calves, her vulva will swell and become flabby and there may be a slight clear discharge. The 'bones' on either side of the tail head will drop and you can slip the side of your hand into the cavities. These are not actually bones but ligaments relaxing to allow the pelvis outlet to stretch for the birth. If you want to calve indoors, get her in now. Sometimes, however, the act of bringing her in puts her off for a day or two. Rosie gets a dreamy faraway look in her eyes the day before she calves and is more than usually affectionate.

If she is calving in the field she might wander about as though looking for a good nursery, but some cows seem to be taken completely by surprise and make no preparation at all. She will probably look for a sheltered copse or bushes. It is not unknown for an experienced stockman to be unaware of a calving because the calf has been hidden in a safe patch of brambles where it will remain completely still and silent even if its mother is removed from the field.

In the majority of cases the cow will calve quite easily and quickly by herself, without any help from you, though she might appreciate a little quiet company. This is particularly the case with a first-calf heifer: it is said that a heifer will allow herself to be milked only by the person who kept her company during the birth.

More often than not you wander down in the morning and find the cow licking a healthy tail-flicking calf as it searches for the elusive udder. But if the cow has any history of calving problems, or if you have put her to a bull liable to produce an outsize calf, stay up all night with her just in case, and warn the vet that you might be calling on his services. Have someone else with you if possible. In any event, this being perhaps your only cow, you will want to be with her. At the very least, check her at intervals and last thing at night.

A normal birth goes like this:

1 The cervix and vagina relax, uterine contractions start, and you will probably see a clear mucus. This stage usually takes about six hours, though in a heifer it might be as much as twenty-four hours.
2 The delivery. The cow now strains in earnest, either lying or standing. The first waterbag bursts to release clear straw-coloured liquid. The second water bag holds the calf in the uterus and is filled with a clear or greyish mucus. The bags might be visible before bursting, or they may burst before they

protrude. Normal delivery of the calf is completed within one-and-a-half hours of the appearance of the first waterbag. The calf should arrive front feet first, followed by the muzzle at about knee level. After delivery the cow starts to wash the calf.
3 The placenta is ejected, normally within six to twelve hours of the birth.

Fig 9 The normal presentation of a calf is with the forefeet emerging first, followed by the nose at about the level of the knees. If the calf is wrongly presented, skilled manipulation is needed to adjust the position. In the case of twins, the second calf may correctly emerge hind feet first.

Do not interfere until the cow is obviously in labour and the first waterbag has burst without any sign of a calf. If the cow has been straining for more than an hour, scrub up to your elbows, soap your hands and arms, and explore. If you can feel two feet and a nose, let her try for another quarter of an hour, then slip loops of clean cord over the calf's feet above the fetlock and pull *in time with the cow's contractions*, pulling each leg alternately to help ease the calf's shoulders through the pelvis. It might take three people at this stage, and could last for ten or twenty minutes. Get the vet if in any doubt.

If on exploration you find that the calf is wrongly presented, you need expert help. It may be that one or both forelegs are bent back and to one side, or the calf is presented back to front. Perhaps the calf is just too big for the cow. A wrong presentation can be dealt with: an outsize calf is a vet's nightmare. A bent leg can be manipulated into the right position while it is still floating in the foetal fluids. If the fluids have a yellow-brown stain, time is short: the calf is in need of oxygen.

After the calf is born, the cow should attend to it after a few minutes' rest. If she does not, it is up to you to clear any mucus from its nostrils and to help it dry off by rubbing it down. If necessary, you can tickle out its first breath by slipping a clean straw 2–3in up its nostril. The calf will try to stand within an hour or so: let it do what it wants. In fact, interference is always best avoided – let the pair of them sort things out.

Do watch, however, to make sure that the calf finds the udder and suckles as soon as possible, in any event within the first six hours of its life. This first meal is vital: it gives the calf life-saving antibodies and gets the system going. You will find black jelly-like droppings which indicate that the calf has suckled. At first the calf may have trouble in locating the udder: it will latch on to any part of the cow's body within reach, which could be thigh or belly rather than teat. It should learn, but be prepared to teach it if it does not. While it suckles, the mother will probably give its bottom a good wash, thus both cleaning it and encouraging it to defecate.

There is no need to worry about the umbilical cord. Dip it in iodine as a precaution against infection. Normally the residual cord is about 8in long and will shrivel up and drop off a week or so after the birth.

If the cow has calved in the field, you can lure her indoors by picking up the calf (one arm round its buttocks and one round its chest) and walking slowly ahead of the cow, letting her sniff the calf and avoiding getting her agitated. You may prefer to leave them both in the field if the weather is dry, but it is advisable to have some sort of control over the calf within the first few days or it will become wild and wilful.

For the first four days after calving the cow produces the sticky yellow milk known as colostrum, which is vital to the calf and protects it from all manner of infections. If the calf does not suckle within hours of birth, milk the cow and bottle-feed the calf to ensure that it does receive colostrum. Otherwise do not milk for the first day or two unless the cow is really bursting: let the calf have all it can get. In any event do not milk the cow right out for the first few days.

Within two days of calving, and usually within twelve hours, the cow will cleanse, that is, pass out the afterbirth. Left to her own devices, she will eat it. Her natural urge is to disguise the fact of birth from predators. If she has not cleansed by the third or fourth day, get the vet: retained afterbirth sets up infection and can cause severe problems.

After the birth there is a period of potential risk for the cow, though in the case of a house cow the risk is greatly reduced. When a cow calves she begins immediately to produce milk. The output increases quickly and the cow tends to lose a lot of calcium fast, which can give rise to milk fever. She will show signs of abnormal nervousness and will 'paddle' her feet. Death can follow quickly so get the vet as soon as you notice the symptoms. Try to keep her on her feet without agitating her too much. If she does go down, try to prop her in an upright position to avoid bloat or inhalation of regurgitated stomach contents. If you inspect her at 11pm and 7am during the first week after calving, you should not lose her from milk fever during the night. However, assuming you have not steamed up too much, and if you have refrained from grabbing all the milk out of her anyway, there should be no problem.

A serious, though rare, complication, is uterine prolapse when the uterus itself hangs inside out from the vulva, reaching down to the hocks. Keep the prolapse clean and undamaged and get the vet immediately.

You may find that a cow's appetite is poor for a day or two after calving. She should pick up within a few days: encourage her with tasty food, with molasses as an appetiser. It is sound practice to continue to feed her on the same type of concentrates as those used for steaming up in order to avoid any digestive problems. To avoid loss of condition, feed as if she is giving half a gallon more than she actually is.

Now the heart searching begins: the fate of the calf. In any event leave it with the cow for at least a couple of days so that it can take full advantage of the colostrum and additional antibodies acquired from close contact with its mother. Unless you intend to leave the calf on the cow until it is weaned, take it away after the first two or three days, because the longer you leave them together the more cruel the parting. Remove the calf to a warm calf box, tying up the mother while you do so to frustrate her protective instincts.

The cow will bawl furiously for a couple of days. Make sure the calf is out of earshot because hearing her own calf will make matters ten times worse and she will make strenuous efforts to reach it. She may be reluctant to let her milk down for you but be patient and persist. She will settle down in due course.

8 Calf Care

Raising a calf is a good way of making the best of excess milk, but it requires patience, accommodation, scrupulous hygiene, luck, and a clear idea of the calf's ultimate destiny. Make up your mind whether you want beef or milk, and whether you are raising to the weaning stage at two or three months, or to a 'finished' stage (that is, ready to calve or fit for slaughter) at two or two-and-a-half years.

There are several methods of raising a calf but if you only have one productive house cow and want milk for the house your choice is reduced to hand rearing, limited access suckling, or natural suckling.

Whatever the method, your first requirement is suitable housing. A calf running with its mother can survive quite happily in the field at any time of year, as long as it has access to a dry bed in wet weather. Provide a shelter which only the calf has access to; you can make this out of straw bales, two or three high, arranged in bonded fashion on three sides, with a couple of old doors (paint-free) for a roof held in place with more bales. Protect it so that older stock cannot butt or scratch against the bales, and allow the calf access through a 'creep', that is, a rail under which the calf can pass easily but which is too low for other animals.

If a calf is separated from its mother, so that you are feeding it yourself, it will still thrive in a field with a bale shelter (give it other calves for company) but it may be more convenient to raise the calf indoors. You want a warm, airy, dry shed with adequate ventilation but no draughts. Litter generously with soft straw, and clean out regularly. If you are raising more than one calf, let each one have its own pen within the shed so that it can get all the feed it deserves without being bullied. You can make pens by dividing the area with straw bales or wooden barriers. It may be necessary to clad railed partitions to avoid draughts, but remember that the calves need to be able to see each other and preferably touch each other. All wood should be creosoted and disinfected regularly by scrubbing down with Jeyes fluid. Hygiene is essential.

There are manufactured disposable pens, which are made of tough cardboard and are burnt after the calf has finished with them: they are effective, but in the long term expensive. For a newly-born calf you can build an 'igloo' of straw bales within the shed, or provide an infra-red lamp to keep it warm. Keep it separate from other calves until its disease resistance is established.

It is desirable for the shed to have a run outside, facing south for maximum sunshine, so that the calf can get fresh air and benefit from the vitamin D provided by the sun's rays, which helps to build up strong bones.

Natural Suckling

With this method you leave the calf with the cow until the calf is eight or twelve weeks old. Suckled calves go ahead quickly compared to hand-reared calves, but there are problems. What about your own milk supply? The calf will suck when she feels like it, at least three times a day, but she will not choose regular times so you will never know when there is enough in the bag for you.

Another problem with suckling is weaning. To separate the animals when they have been together for up to three months will cause distress to both of them. If they stay together the calf will go on suckling until the mother kicks it off, and it is not unnatural for a two-year-old to attempt to suckle. In some dairy herds, freshly calved heifers joining the milking herd can be quite a nuisance when they start suckling, even if they were reared on the bucket. In these situations farmers fit a variety of anti-sucking devices, such as a plain self-piercing ring through the nose, a spiked noseband, or a plate which flaps from the nose and allows the animal to graze but not to suck. But an intelligent heifer can master such devices, and anyway all these are designed for the older heifer and are no good as a disincentive to a twelve-week-old calf that you are trying to wean.

You can 'batch' suckle, that is, give the freshly calved cow two calves to run with (no milk for you this way) for about six weeks, then remove the calves and put on two more. You can keep

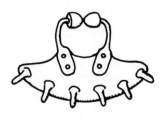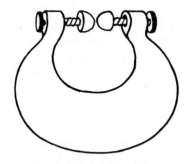

Fig 10 Two examples of devices fitted to older heifers which attempt to suckle milking cows. Both are fixed into the nostrils by means of spring-held or screw-adjusted clamps. One has blunted spikes; the other has a plate which flaps on hinges and prevents suckling (which requires an upward tilt of the muzzle) but allows the heifer to graze without hindrance. Not suitable for calves. An alternative is to use a head collar with blunted galvanised nails protruding from the noseband.

rotating like this as long as the cow and the milk supply allow. To get the cow to accept a calf which is not its own can be a problem, and people have tried all sorts of ruses, even blindfolding the cow and drenching the alien calf in eau de Cologne to disguise its smell.

Limited Access Suckling

Keep the cow and calf separate. At the usual milking times bring the cow inside and let the calf suck for a while (three times a day for the first two weeks of the calf's life). Then wash down the udder and take the rest of the milk – and all the cream – for yourself. Alternatively, milk two or three teats then leave the calf with its mother for twenty minutes or so to use up the rest of the milk. The main problem is that you do not know exactly how much milk the calf is getting. You might also find that the cow does not like the idea and either kicks off the calf or plays hell when you milk. Further, a frustrated calf might persist with a milked-out teat and damage it.

After a couple of weeks tether the calf and the cow in the field so that the calf can learn to graze by example, get used to a halter, and be weaned gradually: let it suck twice a day for a couple of weeks, then reduce to once a day, lessening the suckling time by stages until the calf is weaned at, say, eight weeks. It is useful to get a young calf accustomed to being tied up, whether by neck collar or, preferably, head collar. Calves are amenable only when young: later they are difficult to train – and strong.

Another way of keeping a cow and calf separate but content is to build a small cow-proof calf shed in the field, designed so that the cow can maintain contact and wash the calf but the calf cannot reach the udder although she can see the cow in any part of the field. An example of such a shed is shown on page 72. It is designed so that the calf can be confined in the shed or allowed into a small, railed paddock. In due course the calf can be given a larger grazing area by the use of electric fencing to keep her separate from the cow.

Bottle- and Bucket-Feeding

Hand rearing may avoid some of the weaning problems outlined above because the calf does not touch the udder after the first two or three days. The calf should be kept completely separate from the cow, and out of earshot.

For bottle-feeding you need a good supply of large squash bottles and a couple of rubber calf teats. Make sure the bottles and teats are always scrupulously clean. It may be necessary to enlarge the holes in the teats using a hot steel knitting needle.

By depriving the calf of the udder you are inviting trouble and you must be very alert to the problems of infection. Use the mother's milk for preference, because it provides natural antibodies. You can use special calf-raising milk powders if you wish: dilute according to the manufacturer's instructions.

The greatest advantage of hand rearing is that you know exactly how much milk the calf is getting, and in both economic and health terms this is important. A four-day-old calf should get 1lb milk for every 10lb live bodyweight. (There are 10lb milk to the gallon.) A Jersey calf needs about 5pt a day, a Dexter 6pt and a Friesian 8pt. Maintain this level to the age of three weeks. (A word of caution: the Jersey Cattle Society warns against overfeeding dairy heifer calves on the grounds that the animal may become a poor milker, putting too much weight on its bag.)

Feed the calf three times a day for the first week or two, then reduce to twice a day. The milk must be fed at a consistent temperature. Keep the feed bottles in a bucket of warm water to maintain the temperature between 95°F (35°C) and 100°F (37·8°C). Consistency of temperature is important; it is also important to be consistent in the quality of milk fed – whole, skimmed, diluted, or powdered. If you wish to make changes, whether in quality, temperature or quantity, do so gradually.

Bottle-feeding should be readily accepted by the calf, as sucking is the natural urge. Use your commonsense: be gentle, patient and firm; hold the bottle at a steady angle so that the calf can suck easily but does not choke on the milk. Remember that for the first four days the calf must have colostrum and should receive a minimum of 4pt in its first twenty-four hours of life. As a substitute for colostrum, you can feed the calf an egg whipped in water daily for ten days, or ask the vet to give a serum injection.

The principles of bucket-feeding are the same as bottle-feeding, but the initial stages of training the calf to the bucket require more patience. Be prepared to spend a lot of time over the first few feeds and make sure you do have a bucket of hot water handy to keep the milk warm. Let the calf suck your clean fingers; with your hand cupped up to the muzzle. Gradually lower your hand to the bucket so that the calf is still sucking as its mouth reaches the milk. Eventually you will be able to withdraw your fingers and let the calf drink the milk on its own, but it might take several attempts.

Make sure the calf has access to fresh water at all times, though it may not be interested until it is about two weeks old.

Do not increase the milk ration as the calf grows: encourage it to eat roughage and concentrates. A calf is physically capable of nibbling hay or grass at ten days old but it is not sure what to do with it. It is important that it has the opportunity to explore and learn: its rumen will not develop unless it begins to take in some roughage. Offer it very good hay in small quantities.

Fig 11 illustrates the four stomachs which ruminants have – the rumen, the reticulum and the omasum (the 'auxiliary' stomachs), and the abomasum – and it is important to have some understanding of their functions.

In a mature cow the largest stomach is the rumen, in which roughage is stored during grazing and where it is partly broken down by enzymes before being returned to the mouth as a cud for chewing. The reticulum, which is much smaller, tends to store indigestible objects; it is known to the butcher as tripe. The omasum is the third chamber where the breaking-down process is continued. The abomasum is the true digestive stomach, which contributes pepsin to break down the protein in the food before it passes into the small intestine.

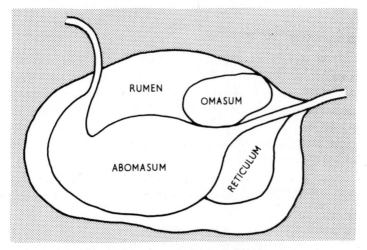

Fig 11 The stomachs of a newborn calf

In the newborn calf, the abomasum is the only one of the four stomachs which really functions, the other three being small and undeveloped. Milk bypasses the rumen and goes direct to the abomasum, where it is curdled by rennet to make it more digestible to the calf. A suckling calf takes milk at frequent intervals and is able to form several small curds regularly, which are easily digested. A bucket-fed calf may drink too quickly, or too much at one time, and the result can be one large curd in the abomasum which is not digested. The curd is further enlarged at the next feed. This indigestible lump can be a cause of scouring in bucket-fed calves.

When the calf begins to eat fibrous foods, such as grass and hay, these go into the rumen to be broken down by bacteria, and the rumen, omasum and reticulum begin to develop. In due course, they outgrow the abomasum and the calf is able to survive on dry foods.

At about four weeks you can start offering the calf concentrates. Begin with a little – never more than it will eat up – and increase from about $\frac{1}{2}$lb to a maximum of 4lb a day. The concentrates can be either bought-in weaner pellets or a home-mixed ration such as 2 parts flaked maize, $1\frac{1}{2}$ crushed oats, $\frac{3}{4}$ molassed meal, $\frac{3}{4}$ fish meal, and some minerals. The calf may not be interested in concentrates at first. The natural preference is for milk and roughage.

Hay is a step towards grass. Get the calf on to pasture as soon as you can, depending on the time of year. The pasture must be clean, that is, no cattle should have been near it for at least a year, or you may get worm problems. Calves running with their mothers seem to develop their own immunity to worms in the pasture, but calves on their own do not. Talk to the vet about anti-worm measures: it is easier to prevent than cure. If the calf loses condition and starts coughing, it may well have picked up lungworms (husk): house it immediately, feed it well and get the vet.

Spring is an excellent grazing season for youngsters: the grass is at its most digestible and palatable. It does not matter if the weather is still cold (though a calf should not be turned out on to frosted grass or it will get an upset stomach) but if it is wet and windy keep the calf in and feed it on hay. However, grass is both the cheapest and best food after milk, so make the most of it. Remember that unless you have already trained the calf to the halter you will find it difficult to catch or herd it once it has the freedom of a field: keep the grazing area limited, and train the calf to respect an electric fence by tethering it close to the wire for a day or two with the fencer at high strength.

For various reasons it is practical to have a small holding paddock within the field into which the calf can easily be driven, and a useful asset is a 'race' (a narrow passageway) in which the calf can be detained for routine veterinary treatment.

A young calf can find its way under barbed-wire and through gaps in hedges that no cow would even notice. It is more likely to go under a wire than over, so an electric fence should have a second strand of wire below the top strand, and a barbed-wire fence should have at least three strands, including one about 9 or 12in above the ground.

Weaning

A calf cannot survive on dry food until it is at least three weeks old, and it will grow much better on milk for the first two or three months. Before you wean a calf, make sure it is eating at least 1lb concentrates a day, preferably more, and that it can cope with grass or hay (which indicates that its rumen has developed). Reduce the milk ration gradually, by decreasing to one feed a day, or by reducing the quantity in each feed by a total of 1pt a day, or by diluting the mixture. Alternatively, stop the milk all at once; this may cause a check in the calf's progress but it will recover and make up any lost ground quite quickly.

Twelve weeks is a sensible age at which to complete weaning; three weeks is the very earliest at which to start. Beef calves can profitably continue to suckle until they are six months old.

Scouring

Scouring is diarrhoea – in effect an upset stomach caused by bacteria or a virus – and it is highly infectious to other calves. Scouring rarely occurs in suckled calves. Hand-reared animals, however, are at risk from lack of proper cleansing of utensils, lack of care in heating milk, or an excess of milk. At the first sign of scouring, feed a saline solution ($\frac{1}{3}$oz salt to 2pt water) or glucose and warm water, instead of milk. Scouring causes rapid dehydration, so try to compensate for the loss of fluid from the body with adequate warm water on its own. Call the vet: take no chances with a young calf. If you have other calves, keep the pens thoroughly clean in order to curtail the spread of infection.

Scouring does not usually occur once the rumen develops, so early encouragement on to hay or grass is sound practice.

Disbudding

Whether or not you allow a calf to develop its horns is a matter of personal preference. There are practical disadvantages to horns: they can catch in wire, they can spike an udder or eye, and they can encourage a cow to be unduly assertive. Dehorning when the horns are fully developed is a messy and painful business; disbudding a young calf is quick and, if done properly, painless. Get an expert to do it for you unless you have experience. The most satisfactory method is with an electric dehorning iron which burns out the little knobs you can feel at four to six weeks. A local anaesthetic is required under the Protection of Animals (Anaesthetics) Act 1954.

Registration

If you want to register a pedigree calf with the breed society, you should do so before it is two months old. Check with the relevant society for details of fees, conformation requirements, ear numbering, etc.

Vaccination

You should inform the DVO if you have a heifer calf from which you intend to breed, and then give him due warning when she is approaching the age of three months. Under the Brucellosis Eradication Scheme the Ministry gives free S.19 vaccinations to heifers between the ages of 90 and 180 days: it is not compulsory but the Ministry thinks it advisable, though some farmers disagree. It can be given by a Ministry vet or by your own vet. The calf will be fitted with a metal ear tab which identifies her permanently as a vaccinated animal.

Finally, watch out for unlikely hazards. Calves will eat anything as an experiment, including loose hairs from a horse's tail, string, plastic and other indigestible material. The effects can be more than a passing stomach ache, so check regularly that such items are well out of reach. A livestock farmer can shrug off illness as inevitable; the smallholder cannot, in both economical and emotional terms. To the house cow owner, a calf may be the total of his young stock so that the well-being of the individual calf is vital. With sound hygiene and sensible preventive measures, the calf's health should be assured; its owner can then enjoy the calf's development and share its curiosity about the experiences each new day offers.

9 Produce

The house cow owner will have a number of items which can be put to profitable use: live animals, milk and its by-products, and manure.

Live Animals
You can sell privately, by advertising in your local paper, *Farmers Weekly*, or specialist magazines for the self-sufficient. The advantage of a private sale is that you get a chance to meet the prospective buyer and keep in contact. Check *Farmers Weekly* for current average prices, or ask locally.

You can send the animal to market. Small calves can be secured in a sack and carried on the back seat of a car. Larger animals obviously need proper livestock transport; contact a local firm which goes regularly to the market and knows all the procedures.

Any purchaser will need a few pieces of paper, namely, a movement certificate from the Ministry (allow them time to deal with your notification) and relevant accreditation certificates. A purchaser is likely to ask for a vet's certificate of health and documentary evidence that your animals are tuberculin tested. For animals registered with a breed society the new owner will want the registration certificate and you will have to inform the society of the change of ownership and pay a transfer fee. If you are selling an in-calf animal, pass over the AI certificate.

The Ministry's central veterinary laboratories sometimes need animals for experimental purposes. For example, they raise some calves to full breeding status and test the effects of different diets — how vital is colostrum? Does a fat calf make a poor milker? How much energy does a herd animal use up in competing for food? But there is no guarantee of the animal's destiny, nor does the Ministry offer good prices.

Milk

The sale of milk has already been discussed in Chapter 5. Sell butter and cheese to health food shops, farm shops and at local markets. Skim milk and whey will be welcomed by a local pig or chicken farmer, but only on a regular basis.

Manure

You will have plenty of manure! Make a good pile each time you muck out the cow's winter-quarters and pack it down well. Store the manure under cover to keep the rain off so that all the vitality is not washed away. By the following winter the straw and dung will have become a rich, black heap of goodness. *Use* it, and sell the excess in plastic fertiliser bags.

And as well as these profitable commodities, what else? There is the satisfaction in building, creating and tending. There is harmony and enjoyment as well as challenge and sheer hard work. There are those personal experiences, momentary and familiar, that add something intangible. There is sweat, muck, earthiness. Aren't they worthwhile when on a dark winter evening you lean against your cow's flank, hearing the swish of the milk in the pail, feeling her warmth, feeling her unborn calf moving in her belly, and singing your own tuneless milking song under your breath?

Appendix

Breed Societies

Ayrshire Cattle Society of Great Britain and Ireland – PO Box No 8, 1 Racecourse Road, Ayr KA7 2DE

British Friesian Cattle Society of Great Britain and Ireland – Scotsbridge House, Rickmansworth, Herts WD3 3BB

Dexter Cattle Society – Hon Secretary, Lomond, Seckington Lane, Newton Regis, Tamworth, Staffs B79 0ND

English Guernsey Cattle Society – The Bury Farm, Pednor Road, Chesham, Bucks HP5 2LA

Jersey Cattle Society of the United Kingdom – Jersey House, 154 Castle Hill, Reading, Berks RG1 7RP

Shorthorn Society of the United Kingdom of Great Britain and Ireland – 11 Priory Terrace, Leamington Spa, Warwickshire CV31 1BA

Welsh Black Cattle Society (Cymdeithas Gwartheg Duon Cymreig) – 13 Bangor Street, Caernarfon, Gwynedd LL55 1AP

Useful Addresses

Clares Carlton Ltd (cheese-making equipment) – Wells, Somerset BA5 1SQ and 7 Winchester Avenue, Denny, Stirlingshire

Dalton Supplies Ltd (identification tags, handling aids, instruments) – Nettlebed, Henley-on-Thames, Oxfordshire

R. J. Fullwood & Bland (rennet) – 25 Bevenden Street, London W1 and Ellesmere, Shropshire

Richard List (galvanised calf pens, house cow handling equipment) – Godington, Bicester, Oxfordshire OX6 9AF

Self-Sufficiency & Smallholding Supplies (smallholder's supplies) – The Old Palace, Priory Road, Wells, Somerset BA5 1FY

Small Scale Supplies (home dairy equipment) – Widdington, Saffron Walden, Essex

Her Majesty's Stationery Office – PO Box 569, London SE1 9NH

Landsmans Bookshop Ltd (postal bookshop for farmers and gardeners) Buckenhill, Bromyard, Herefordshire

Practical Self-Sufficiency (forum for smallholders, published six times a year) – Broadleys Publishing Company, Widdington, Saffron Walden, Essex CB11 3SP

Milk Marketing Board – Thames Ditton, Surrey KT7 0EL
Ministry of Agriculture, Fisheries & Food –
    Publications: Tolcarne Drive, Pinner, Middlesex HA5 2DT
    Regional Offices:
    Eastern Region, Block C, Government Buildings, Brooklands Avenue, Cambridge CB2 2DR
    East Midland Region, Block 2, Government Buildings, Chalfont Drive, Nottingham NG8 3RH
    Northern Region, Government Buildings, Kenton Bar, Newcastle-upon-Tyne NE1 2YA
    South Eastern Region, Block A, Government Offices, Coley Park, Reading RG1 6DT
    South Western Region, Block 3, Government Buildings, Burghill Road, Westbury-on-Trym, Bristol BS10 6NJ
    West Midland Region, Woodthorne, Wolverhampton WV6 8TQ
    Yorks & Lancs Region, Block 2, Government Buildings, Lawnswood, Leeds LS16 5PY
    Wales, Plas Crug, Aberystwyth, Dyfed SY23 1NG

APPENDIX

Brucellosis Eradication Scheme

The Ministry of Agriculture, Fisheries & Food (MAFF) is attempting to eradicate brucellosis (contagious abortion) from England and Wales. As part of the eradication scheme, no animal can be moved from one premises to another – be it to a new owner, a show, a market, or your own field which happens to be on the other side of the county boundary – without a movement permit from the Ministry.

There are three types of movement permit:

1 For accredited cattle
2 For non-accredited cattle aged six months and over
3 For non-accredited cattle aged under six months

Whenever possible, buy from an accredited herd, that is, one that has been tested by the Ministry and found free of brucellosis. Accredited animals can be moved to your own premises quite simply, accompanied by a copy of the movement permit, as long as your own premises are clear within the scheme, which they will be if you have never had cattle and if any neighbouring cattle are at least two fences away. The Ministry will inspect these premises before the movement. In other circumstances ask your Ministry District Veterinary Officer (DVO) for advice.

Non-accredited cattle require a more complex procedure.

Aged six months and over
1 Not more than fourteen days before the anticipated movement, you must have a private blood test of the animal by a Ministry-approved laboratory. Your own vet may take the blood sample. If the test is positive, do not buy the animal. If it is negative, apply for a movement permit.
2 After the approved movement has taken place, notify the DVO of the date of the animal's arrival on your premises. The animal must be kept in isolation from other cattle for at least sixty days. If the animal is pregnant the isolation period is sixty days or until fourteen days after calving, whichever is the longer. Then it must have another private blood test at an approved laboratory, the result being sent forthwith to the Ministry.
3 If this test is negative the Ministry will authorise you to let the animal join the rest of the 'herd'.
4 If the test is inconclusive, the animal must continue to be isolated and will have to be retested. If the test is positive, the animal must be slaughtered under the Ministry's specifications and the isolation premises must be extensively disinfected.

Calves under six months
Rule number 1 above applies but thereafter isolation is not necessary.

103

APPENDIX

Once you are accredited you will be given a number, and a movements record book in which you must record all cattle movements to and from the premises, having obtained permits on each occasion. In theory the Ministry can then trace the movement history of any animal at any time, which is important in the case of an outbreak of the disease. The Ministry reserves the right to check your movements record book at intervals. Once a year your 'herd' will be retested by the Ministry, free of charge; reactors will be slaughtered and you will receive partial compensation.

Bovine Tuberculosis

Your 'herd' will be tested for tuberculosis when it is first established and thereafter every three years. Reactors are slaughtered and you receive partial compensation. The herd must be tuberculin tested (TT) before you can consider selling milk.

The Ministry will give your herd a 'herd mark' — usually two letters identifying the area followed by numbers identifying your particular herd — and your cattle must bear this identification followed by a different serial number (starting with '1') for every animal in the herd. Any calves born on the premises may, if you wish, be marked with the herd mark, then a letter indicating year of birth, then a serial number indicating the order of birth in that year. Calves must be marked by the age of two weeks by one system or another: the Ministry will supply details of approved methods of ear tagging and ear tattooing.

All cattle must be identifiable from permanent ear marking. However, an animal registered with its breed society will be allocated an ear number by the society, and this can be used instead of the Ministry number.

APPENDIX

Calculation of Rations:
Starch/Protein Equivalents

(Source: *Rations for Livestock*, MAFF Bulletin No 48)

The starch equivalent (SE) and protein equivalent (PE) of some of the more common feedingstuffs are set out below. The daily requirements for a milk-producing animal are:

Maintenance
(These figures include a nominal 1lb allowance in SE for energy expended on grazing and exercise.)

Breed	Liveweight (cwt)	Total SE (lb)	Total PE (lb)
Dexter	5·8	5·4	0·39
Jersey	7·1	6·1	0·48
Guernsey	8·5	6·8	0·6
Ayrshire	9·5	7·2	0·67
Shorthorn	10·5	7·75	0·72
Friesian	11·5	8·3	0·78

Production
(Simplified averages based on butterfat content of milk)
Rations for each gallon:

	SE	PE
Channel Islands breeds	3·0	0·7
Other breeds	2·5	0·5

For example, a Jersey giving 3 gallons of milk requires:

Maintenance (M):	SE 6·1 /	PE 0·48
Production:	SE 9·0 /	PE 0·21
Total requirement:	SE 15·1 /	PE 0·69

If your stocks allow her a ration of, say, 12lb a day of medium meadow hay (SE 32/PE 3·6) she will be getting from hay:

$$\text{SE: } \frac{12 \times 32}{100} = 3.84 \qquad \text{PE: } \frac{12 \times 3.6}{100} = 0.432$$

This will give her enough PE for maintenance only, but not nearly enough SE for maintenance, and nothing towards the production ration. Give her in addition enough barley (SE 71/PE 6·5) to bring the total to the right levels for, say, maintenance plus the first $\frac{1}{2}$gal milk (SE: $6·1 + [\frac{1}{2} \times 3·0] = 7·6$/PE: $0·48 + [\frac{1}{2} \times 0·7] = 0·83$):

12lb hay gives: SE: $\dfrac{12 \times 32}{100} = 3 \cdot 84$ PE: $\dfrac{12 \times 3 \cdot 6}{100} = 0 \cdot 432$

6lb barley gives: SE: $\dfrac{6 \times 71}{100} = 4 \cdot 26$ PE: $\dfrac{6 \times 6 \cdot 5}{100} = 0 \cdot 390$

Total SE: $\overline{8 \cdot 10}$ Total PE: $\overline{0 \cdot 822}$

The PE is correct for M + $\frac{1}{2}$; the SE is a little high but no matter. Now add a 16 per cent dairy cake at $4\frac{1}{2}$lb per gallon for the production over that first $\frac{1}{2}$gal, that is for $2\frac{1}{2}$gal give about 10lb cake, so that the final daily ration will be:

12lb hay + 6lb barley + 10lb dairy cake

You will see that this system allows for an infinite number of combinations, and the challenge is to juggle available feedingstuffs until the total combined SE and PE is that required for the particular animal's productivity.

Table of Feedingstuffs

Type of Food		Dry Matter (%)	SE per 100lb	PE per 100lb
Roots:	Carrots	13·0	8·8	0·6
	Mangels (white flesh)	10·7	5·5	0·4
	Mangels (yellow flesh)	13·2	6·8	0·4
	Potatoes	23·8	18·5	0·8
	Sugarbeet	23·4	15·0	0·5
	Swedes	11·5	7·3	0·7
	Turnips	8·5	4·4	0·4
Root leaves:	Mangels	11·0	5·3	1·3
	Sugarbeet tops	16·2	8·6	1·1
	Turnip	11·6	5·3	0·9
Greens:	Cabbage, drumhead	11·0	6·6	0·9
	Comfrey	11·5	5·2	1·2
	Kale, thousandhead	16·0	10·0	1·5
	Kale, marrowstem	14·0	9·1	1·4
Grass:	Close-grazed, non-rotational	20·0	14·7	4·1
	Extensive grazing, spring	20·0	11·2	2·1
	Extensive grazing, winter	20·0	11·4	1·7
Silage:	Grass, first quality	20·0	12·2	2·6
	Lucerne	25·0	11·1	2·8
	Maize	20·0	9·3	0·9
	Pea haulms and pods	25·0	12·3	2·1

APPENDIX

Type of Food		Dry Matter (%)	SE per 100lb	PE per 100lb
Hay:	Meadow, excellent	85·0	49	7·9
	Meadow, medium	85·0	32	3·6
	Meadow, very poor	85·0	22	2·4
	Seeds hay (ryegrass/clover)	85·0	30	4·8
Straw:	Spring barley	86·0	23	0·7
	Spring oat	86·0	20	0·9
	Winter oat	86·0	21	0·5
	Wheat	86·0	13	0·1
Grains:	Barley	85·0	71·0	6·5
	Maize	87·0	77·6	7·6
	Oats	87·0	59·6	7·6
	Flaked maize	89·0	84·0	9·2
By-products:	Barley, fresh brewers grains	32·4	18·4	5·3
	Barley, dried brewers grains	89·7	48·3	12·5
	Barley, fresh distillers grains	26·2	16·2	6·0
	Barley, dried distillers grains	92·0	57·2	19·1
	Maize bran	88·2	67·0	5·1
	Maize gluten feed	89·6	75·6	19·2
	Maize gluten meal	90·0	81·5	30·4
	Oat bran	90·5	45·5	3·8
	Sugarbeet pulp, wet	15·0	11·7	1·0
	Sugarbeet pulp, dried	90·0	60·0	5·0
	Sugarbeet pulp, molassed	90·0	58·3	4·6
	Wheat bran, fourth grade	87·0	42·6	9·9

NOTE Some statutory definitions of feedingstuffs:

Dried brewers grains – the article produced by drying the residue of malted and unmalted cereals used in brewing, to which no other matter has been added.

Dried distillery grains – ditto, from distillery mash-tuns.

Dried plain beet pulp – the article produced by drying the sugarbeet residue produced in the manufacture of sugar from sugarbeet, with or without the addition of molasses, to give less than 10 per cent of sugar.

Dried molassed beet pulp – ditto, but with the addition of molasses to give 10 per cent or more of sugar.

Flaked maize – the product obtained by cooking and flaking pure maize or Indian corn.

Maize gluten feed – a by-product from the removal of starch and germ from maize.

APPENDIX

Calculation of Rations:
Metabolisable Energy

Metabolisable energy (ME) is defined as the digestible energy of a feed less the energy required to make faeces, urine and methane. It is measured in megajoules (MJ) and the ME values of different feeds are expressed as the number of megajoules in a kilogram of dry matter (MJ/kg DM). In the metric system, dry matter content is based on the number of grams of dry matter in a kilogram of fresh food. To convert a given dry matter percentage into weight, multiply by 10 (for example, if the feed has 85 per cent DM, the metric equivalent is 850g in 1kg DM).

To calculate rations for maintenance, use Table 1 as a basis to estimate the total ME according to the cow's liveweight. Then work out a ration of available feedstuffs: the ME and DM of various feeds are given in Table 3. Check that the cow has sufficient 'appetite' to eat the proposed ration (Table 4).

To include rations for production, you need to know the expected milk yield and the quality of the milk. Table 2 tells you how much ME your cow needs for her expected yield.

Table 1

Daily maintenance allowance for dairy cows

Bodyweight (kg)	Breed (average weight) (kg)	MJ
250		31
300	Dexter (300)	36
350		40
400	Jersey (380)	45
450	Guernsey (450)	49
500	Dairy Shorthorn (500)	54
550	Ayrshire (520)	59
600		63
650		67
700	Friesian (700)	72
	Welsh Black (700)	

Table 2

ME allowance for 1 kg milk (MJ)

Butter fat g/kg	30	35	40	45	50
*SNF g/kg					
84	4·5	4·7	5·1	5·4	5·8
86	4·6	4·9	5·2	5·5	5·9
88	4·6	4·9	5·3	5·6	5·9
90	4·7	5·0	5·3	5·7	6·0
92	4·8	5·1	5·4	5·7	6·1
94	4·8	5·2	5·5	5·8	6·1

NOTE   *SNF = 'solids-not-fat' content of milk.

APPENDIX

Possible breed averages of BF/SNF are:

	Butter fat	SNF	ME allowance
Channel Islands	4·8	9·1	5·90
Dairy Shorthorn	3·6	8·7	4·97
Ayrshire	3·7	8·8	5·07
Friesian	3·5	8·6	4·87

Table 3
Nutritional Value of Feeds

Feed	Dry matter gm/kg	ME MJ/kg DM
Barley	860	13·7
Brewers grains (fresh)	220	10·0
Dried grass	900	10·6
Grazing (ryegrass pasture)	200	12·1
Hay – good	850	10·1
Kale (thousandhead)	160	11·1
Kale (marrowstem)	140	11·0
Maize	190	8·8
Oats	860	11·5
Potatoes	210	12·5
Straw (spring barley)	860	7·3
Straw (winter barley)	860	5·8
Silage (grass) – good	200	10·2
Silage (grass) – poor	200	7·6
Silage (maize)	210	10·8
Sugarbeet pulp (dried)	900	12·7
Swedes and turnips	120	12·8

Table 4
Probable dry matter intake of cow in mid and late lactation (kg/day)

Liveweight (kg)	Milk yield (kg/day)				
	5	10	15	20	25
350	9·3	9·8	10·3	10·8	11·3
400	10·5	11·0	11·5	12·0	12·5
450	11·8	12·3	12·8	13·3	13·8
500	13·0	13·5	14·0	14·5	15·0
550	14·3	14·8	15·3	15·8	16·3
600	15·5	16·0	16·5	17·0	17·5
650	16·8	17·3	17·8	18·3	18·8
700	18·0	18·5	19·0	19·5	20·0

APPENDIX

Table 5

Average metric bodyweights of various breeds

Dexter	300 kg
Jersey	380 kg
Guernsey	450 kg
Dairy Shorthorn	500 kg
Ayrshire	520 kg
Friesian	700 kg
Welsh Black	700+ kg

Table 6

Metric equivalents

1 lb = 0·45 kg
1 cwt = 50·8 kg
1 pt = 0·57 l
1 gal = 4·5 l

Grass Table

Time	Natural stage of growth	Digestibility	Remarks
April	4–6in	80–85%	Restrict grazing to avoid bloat.
May	6–8in	80%	
June	8in or more	70%	Keep topped unless making hay. Hay best made now.
Mid-summer		65%	
Autumn		60%	Limited feeding value – start giving hay.
Late autumn			Give hay for maintenance ration.

APPENDIX

Poisonous Plants

The following plants remain poisonous even after drying and storage, for example, in hay:

Bracken (green)
Bryony, white
Buckthorn
Cowbane and water dropwort
Flax
Foxglove
Horsetails
Lily of the valley
Lupin
Pink family (soapwort, corncockle, sandwort, chickweed)
Poppy family
Ragwort
Ranunculus family (hellebore, columbine, aconite)
Thornapple, henbane, nightshade
Yew

The second list includes plants which are poisonous only when growing: most are only a problem if eaten in quantity.

Kale, rape and fodder beet in excess
Fresh sugarbeet tops
Mangels direct from the ground
Green potatoes
Potato stems and leaves
Tomato stems and leaves

Ash keys and fallen leaves
Oak leaves, particularly in spring ⎰ Give rise to very strong craving
Oak acorns ⎱ after poisoning
Spindle
Box
Ivy (though one young branch can be a good tonic for a sick animal)
Mistletoe berries
Privet
Rhododendron

Buckwheat (for animals with lightly pigmented skins; for example, black-and-white)
Bulbs, rhizomes and corms
Broomrape
Charlock, white mustard, wild radish, horseradish
Hemlock

Houndstongue
Hypericum
Meadow saffron
Rushes (hard)
Sedum
Sorrels
Spurges and mercuries
Ranunculus family (traveller's joy, pheasant's eye, buttercups, marsh marigold, baneberry)
Tobacco
Water figwort

Plants which Affect Milk

These plants may taint the milk (feed *after* milking) or cause problems with butter-churning or cheese-making:

Buttercups
Butterwort
Chamomile
Chervil
Cow wheat
Fool's parsley
Garlic and onion
Hedge mustard
Ivy
Knotgrass and knotweed
Lesser watercress
Marsh marigold
Mint (also prevents clotting and curding)
Ox-eye daisy
Pennycress
Pepper saxifrage
Sage
Sorrel (butter-making problems)
Spurge
Sugarbeet pulp and tops in excess
Tansy
Turnips
Water parsnip
Wild radish
Wood sorrel (churning problems)
Wormwood
Yarrow

APPENDIX

Breeding

To put some beef on to a Channel Islands calf, cross the mother with one of the following breeds:

Aberdeen Angus
Ideal for a first-calf heifer, as the calf will be small. Pure-bred Angus gives top-quality beef.

Charolais
Can produce an outsize calf so select the bull carefully to avoid calving problems. Slow to raise on grass.

Hereford
Produces the typical white-face calf which butchers favour. Choose the bull with care to avoid calving problems.

Limousin
Excellent cross: few calving problems, even with larger calves. Calf easy and quick to rear.

Simmental
Can give problems, both in calving and rearing.

Sussex
A good cross, particularly if raised on summer grass and finished on silage and barley in winter.

Glossary

Acetonaemia A metabolic disorder caused by low glucose levels in the blood

Afterbirth The placenta, or membranes connecting the calf with the dam while in the womb

Aftermath Grazeable growth after harvesting for hay, silage or grain

Anthrax Usually fatal disease, symptoms of which are high fever, enlarged spleen, and swelling of throat; also affects humans

Bag Udder

Bagging Up Rapid filling of the udder shortly before calving

Beestings Colostrum milk

Bloat (or Blow) Condition in which fermentation gases accumulate in the rumen and distend it

Bobby A very young calf sold for meat

Brucellosis Contagious abortion in cattle; can cause undulant fever in humans

Bulldog Calf Abnormal calf with short limbs, swollen abdomen, and foreshortened 'bulldog' jaws: a hereditary condition

Bulling A 'bulling' cow is one which is on heat

Bullock Castrated bull

Calf Young cow or bull up to perhaps ten months old

Cleansing Expulsion of the afterbirth after calving

Colostrum Milk produced for three or four days after calving, rich in vitamins and antibodies

Concentrates Feedingstuffs with high concentration of nutrients in small quantity, high in energy and/or protein

Cross-Breeding Breeding from a cow of one pure breed and a bull of another

Down-Calver A cow or heifer nearing calving

Dry Not giving milk

Empty Not pregnant

Fodder Stalk, leaves and seedhead of a grain crop

Foot-and-Mouth Highly infectious disease; symptoms are blisters on mouth and feet causing salivation and lameness

Freemartin Sterile heifer born as twin to a bull calf

Gadding Restlessness caused by fly irritation

Grade Up Build a pedigree herd from non-pedigree by repeated use of pedigree bulls

Heat Sexual condition of female animal ready to breed

GLOSSARY

Heifer Young cow, usually so defined until the birth of her second calf

Husk Disease caused by parasitic lungworms, giving rise to bronchitis and coughing

Hypocalcaemia Metabolic disorder caused by drop in blood calcium, particularly just after calving, causing partial paralysis resulting in death if not treated; also called milk fever

Hypomagnesaemia Lack of magnesium in the blood stream, causing convulsions and leading to paralysis and death if not treated; also called staggers

In-Calf Pregnant

Mastitis Bacterial infection of the udder; also called garget, mammitis

Milch Cow Milk cow

Milk 85 per cent water, containing some of all the nutrients necessary to maintain life and promote growth (proteins, fats, carbohydrates, minerals and vitamins); one pint supplies about a quarter of the daily recommended intake of protein and all the calcium for a reasonably active man

Milk Fever See **Hypocalcaemia**

Nurse Cow Cow used for suckling calves

Oestrus Sexual heat

Polled Bred without horns

Roughage Feed that is relatively high in fibre (and bulk) and low in nutrients

Scours Diarrhoea

Serve Of a bull, to have sexual intercourse with a cow

Silage Grass and other green crops preserved in a moist, acid state for use as feedstuff, usually stored in a silo (tower or pit)

Skimmed Milk Milk from which most of the butter fat has been removed

Soilage Green crops cut and fed fresh

Solids Non-water content of milk, namely, fat, proteins and minerals

Solids-Not-Fat Total solids in milk less butter fat ('SNF')

Staggers see **Hypomagnesaemia**

Steer Young castrated bull intended for beef

Stirk Young female, 10–20 months old, which has not been served

Stock see **Serve**

Strip To milk out the last drops from the udder

Succulents Wet roughages and roots

Warbles Swellings on animal's back caused by warble fly maggots under the skin

Wean Change from liquid milk diet to solid feed

Zero Grazing Feeding system in which forage is cut and carted to the cow

Book List

Allaby, Michael, *et al. The Survival Handbook* (Macmillan, 1975)
Cobbett, William. *Cottage Economy* (Landsmans Bookshop, 1975)
Ingram, Arthur. *Dairying Bygones* (Shire Publications, 1977)
Russell, Kenneth, *The Herdsman's Book* (Farming Press Ltd, 1974)
——. *Principles of Dairy Farming* (Farming Press Ltd, 1974)
Sainsbury, D. W. B., *et al. Calf Rearing* (Farmers Weekly Publications)
Seymour, John and Sally. *Self-Sufficiency: Art of Producing and Preserving Your Own Food* (Faber, 1973)
Street, Len and Singer, Andrew. *The Backyard Dairy Book* (Prism Press, 1975)
van Loon, Dirk. *The Family Cow* (Garden Way Publishing, 1976)
Vince, John. *Old British Livestock* (Shire Publications, 1976)

Her Majesty's Stationery Office publications:

British Poisonous Plants (Bulletin No 161)
Electric Fencing (Bulletin No 147)
Management of the Dairy Cow (Agricultural Bulletin No 8)
Rations for Livestock (Bulletin No 48)

(Bulletins Nos 8 and 48 are out of print but you should be able to find copies secondhand or at your local library.)

Index

Page numbers in *italics* denote illustrations

Aberdeen Angus, 113
abomasum, 94, *95*
abortion, 69
accreditation, 19, 103-4
acetonaemia, 68
afterbirth, 69, 88
anatomy, *15*
anaemia, 76
anthrax, 77
appetite, 41, 109
artificial insemination, 81
astringents, 76
Ayrshire, 14, 42, 101, *35*

Bagging up, 84
baling, 31
barbed-wire, 22-5
barley, 47
barley equivalents, 43
bedding, 38
beestings, *see* colostrum
bloat, 49, 68
bottle feeding, 93-4
bran, 48
breeds, 13-15, 101
brewers grains, 48
brucellosis, 69, 98, 103
bucket rearing, 94
bulling, 11, 69, 80
butter, 61-3, 100

cabbage, 46
calf care, 90-8
calving, 80-9, *86*
carcasses, 77
cattle plague, 75
Charolais, *36*, 113
cheese, 63-5, 100
clamp, *47*
cleansing, *see* afterbirth
colostrum, 66, 87, 94
concentrates, 42
constipation, 69, 77, 84
cream, 59-60
cross-breeding, 81, 113
cud, loss of, 77

dairy equipment, *61*
Dairy Shorthorn, 14, *36*, 101
Dexter, 13, *18*, 43, 101
diarrhoea, 67, 77

digestive problems, 69
disbudding, *see* horns
discharge, 67, 69, 80
drenching, 78
drying off, 82-3

earmarks, 104
electric fencing, 25-8, *26*

feedstuff values, 106-7, 109
feet, 70, 79
fencing, 22-8, *71*
fertiliser, 29
foot-and-mouth disease, 69, 75
Friesian, 14, 46, *53*, 101

gadding, 22
grains, 47
grass, 28-32, 48-9
grooming, 79
Guernsey, 14, *35*, 101
gynaecology, 69, 88: *see also* calving
    see also discharge

hay, 30-1, 45
hay equivalents, 42
heifers, 16, 82, 83
herbs, 29
Hereford, 113
horns, 97-8
housing, 33, 34-8, *72*
husk, 70, 96
hypocalcaemia, *see* milk fever
hypomagnesaemia, *see* staggers

identification, 104
infusions, 79
injections, 78-9
insemination, 80-1
insurance, 20, 79
itching, 70

Jersey, 13, *18*, 42, 101
joints swollen, 74

kale, 46
kicking, 57, *57*, 58

lactation curve, *43*
lameness, 69, 70
laxatives, 77

lice, 70, 79
limousin, 113
lungworms, 70, 96

magnesium, 49, 70
maintenance ration, 41-2, 105, 108
maize, 47, 48
mange, 70
mangels, 47
manure, 38, 100
market, 75, 99
mastitis, 52, 56, 73
metabolisable energy, 40-1, 108-10
milk, 9, 50-66, 100
milk fever, 73, 88
milking, 34, 39, 50-8, *51*
Milk Marketing Board, 11, 19, 58, 81, 102
milk products, 59-66
milk taints, 44, 112
minerals, 34, 44
Ministry of Agriculture, 19, 75, 81, 99, 102, 103-4
molasses, 47
movement permits, *see* Ministry of Agriculture

New Forest eye, 73

oats, 47
ovulation, 81, *81*

pasteurising, 59
pneumonia, 73, 75
poisoning, 75-7
poisonous plants, 30, 76, 111-12
potatoes, 47
pre-milking, 84
production ration, 42-4, 105, 108
protein equivalent, 40, 105-7
pulse, 67

registration, 98
rennet, 64
ringworm, 74

roots and tubers, 47
rumen, 68, 75, 94-5, *95*

scouring, 95, 97
septicaemia, 74
Shorthorn, *see* Dairy Shorthorn
silage, 31-2, 45
simmental, 113
skimmed milk, 100
slaughter, 77-8
staggers, 49, 70
starch equivalent, 40, 105-7
steaming up, 83
stocking, 80-3
straw, 38, 46
stripping, 55
suckling, 91-3, *92*
sugar beet, 46
Sussex, 113
swedes, 47

teats, *51*, 52, 74, 83
teeth, 16-17
temperature, 67
tethering, 28
training, 27, 94, 96
transport, 20-1
tuberculosis, 74, 77, 104
turnips, 47

udder, 16
umbilical cord, 87
uterus, disorders of, 69, 88

vaccination, 98
vitamins, 44, 91

warbles, 74-5
warts, 74
water, 34, 37, 45, 94
weaning, 92, 97
Welsh Black, 15, *54,* 101
wheat, 47
whey, 100
wire straining, 24
worms, 48, 70, 96